POETOPIA

LONDON & MIDDLESEX

Edited by Donna Samworth

First published in Great Britain in 2015 by:

 Young**Writers**

Remus House
Coltsfoot Drive
Peterborough
PE2 9BF
Telephone: 01733 890066
Website: www.youngwriters.co.uk

Printed and bound in the UK by BookPrintingUK
Website: www.bookprintinguk.com

FOREWORD

Welcome, Reader!

For Young Writers' latest competition, Poetopia, we gave secondary school pupils nationwide the challenge of writing a poem based on the rules of one of 5 factions: Castitas for reflective, honest poetry; Temperantia for angry, assertive poetry; Humilitas for positive, uplifting poetry; Benevolentia for emotional poetry; and Industria for diligent, structured poetry. Poets who wrote a poem outside of these parameters were assigned to Dissimilis.

We chose poems for publication based on style, expression, imagination and technical skill. The result is this entertaining collection full of diverse and imaginative poetry, which is also a delightful keepsake to look back on in years to come.

Here at Young Writers our aim is to encourage creativity in the next generation and to inspire a love of the written word, so it's great to get such an amazing response, with some absolutely fantastic poems. Once all the books in the series are published we will pick the best poem from each faction to win a prize.

I'd like to congratulate all the young poets in Poetopia - London & Middlesex - I hope this inspires them to continue with their creative writing. And who knows, maybe we'll be seeing their names on the best seller lists in the future...

Jenni Bannister
Editorial Manager

THE FACTIONS

CASTITAS (Kas-ti-tas)

- Write a soul-baring, honest poem
- Tell us what it is like to be you
- Channel your confusion and emotions at being a teenager into verse

TEMPERANTIA (Temper-ran-tee-ah)

- Stand up for someone or something
- Vent your anger through poetry
- Express your frustration about a situation that's out of your control

HUMILITAS (Hu-mil-lih-tahs)

- Write a positive, uplifting poem
- Write an ode to celebrate someone or something that you appreciate
- Write a spiritual poem

BENEVOLENTIA (Ben-e-vol-en-tee-ah)

- Write a love / emotional poem
- Empathise with another's situation or predicament
- Write a praise poem
- Write a poem about your best friend / your friendship

INDUSTRIA (In-dust-ree-ah)

- Write a poem about current affairs
- Use a strict poetic form, such as a sonnet or kyrielle
- Research a poet of your choice and write in a similar style

DISSIMĬLIS (Diss-i-mĭl-is)

- If pupils write a poem that falls outside of the factions' rules, they become Dissimĭlis
- Poems can be on any theme or style

CONTENTS

THE
POEMS

The Parallel

There's so much more than the eye can see,
The parallel universe where we just be.
And for something so different we just know,
That we may allow our spirits to grow.

For out in the darkness of the unknown,
There's nothing to fear, we're not alone.
Many worlds that become one
Where we all beat to the same drum.

Aliens, monsters, different folk,
We are all one when you remove the cloak.
Connect to your inner core,
Anything's possible, so much more.

No need to be afraid of what you don't know,
Go out to explore seeds to sow.
At the end of the day we are all one,
From a parallel universe under the sun.

Heartbeat, drum, heartbeat, fly.
Strength to resolve, no fear, don't cry.

Step out, take the mask away,
Confidence to have your say.
March forward, strong and still,
One thing is certain, your own freewill.

At the end of the day we are all one,
From a parallel universe under the sun.

Afton Olivia McKeith-Magaziner

The Unreachable

They want to be like her,
They want to be popular,
To never walk alone:
To be known.

They follow her around,
Do what she says,
Speak like she speaks
And act like she acts.

But when they are gone
She and her friends
Just laugh at them:
They are just scum.

But what I have is better:
I have true friends,
I don't have to try
Or go with the trend.

I can be myself,
Speak as I like,
Do as I like
And I won't be judged.

And we have fun,
Unlike them.
It's just the three of us,
And that is enough.

Karina Uppal (13)

Half Of Me

When you fall, I fall
When you laugh, I laugh
When you smile, I smile
When you cry, I cry
Because half of me is half of you.

When you need me, I come
When you call, I answer
When you speak, I listen
When you yell, I run
Because half of me is half of you.

When you sing, I'm the music
When you cry, I'm the tears
When you talk, I'm the voice
When you think, I'm the brain
Because half of me is half of you.

Our friendship is my world
Our bond is my life
Our memories are my past
Our joy is my future
Because half of me is half of you.

Sunaina Kaur Chohan (14)

The Cold-Hearted

In this barren field
Frozen in time
In a world when you
Where once mine,
As snowflakes fall
No two the same
Just like you
They left as fast as they came,
Hold onto those snowflakes
For they come and they go
In this barren field
Frozen more than you know,
Now in this field
Where I lay
Where you cold-heartedly
Forgot me like yesterday,
Now time is gone
Now we have parted
Fear the empty
And the cold-hearted.

Daniella Teibowei (12)

The Sinister

Murder, disease, it makes me wonder why,
How the world was once a harmonic place,
But now a devastation from on high,
As these people want to laugh in God's face,
Now their preaching has fallen on deaf ears,
What happened in this stranger's hidden mind?
As these people act as if no one cares,
What made them turn to this, what did they find?
And when will they halt? Will they ever learn?
What is the point of killing for pleasure?
Will they realise they'll be left to burn?
What'll be the cost, there is no treasure,
Weapons and bombs it all needs to be ceased,
I surrender, we need justice and peace!

Heaven Constantine (13)

 # Reflection

Her reflection
So different to her appearance
Her reaction
The world looked at her own reflection
She's changed
In so many ways
No one can blame
This immortal game
It will never end
She will be in this constant struggle, there's always trouble
She's scared
It's the end of her existence
Death is persistence
This is the end . . . death, death, death.

Nasim Hassani (12)
Al-Sadiq And Al-Zahra Schools, London

The Spirit Within

What's done is done
What's old has been won
Why worry about these silly little puns
These things they are meaningless
They don't matter
What matters is what you can see
All seen is free
These huge monuments
These buildings
Inventions
Their life
Their blessings
They're only in this moment
Don't worry about the past
Only worry about what you have
There is so much to find in life
Come on, why are you still stuck in that time?
So much to see
So much to be seen
The greater is better
The better is seen
Everything has happened
Now it's time to live the moment
And take a chance
Make it flow
Make it seem like it's your last glance
This world, it won't last eternity
What do you imagine in this mental fraternity?
It will end soon
So come on
Live life for what it is
Not what others have said
Make it seem like this world is only there for one moment
One second
And that second is yours
For infinity and beyond
What the heavens can see is what the eyes can't see
But you can't see Heaven
So don't worry

Live the moment
See what can be seen
Don't shed tears over the past
The past is history
And tomorrow is yet but a mystery
Worry about the moment
Even if you're in trouble
Thank God for it could be double
Celebrate life and enjoy it
Let the doors of Heaven cheer for every action you do
Let them cry when you go to sleep
I bet you already knew
Be the greatest, the most optimistic
You are what the heavens needed all these years
All these centuries
All these tears
You're what has been pleaded for
You're the only one needed
Be the one that even the gods bow down to
Be the one known for what's best in this world
With that amazing smile
Wow, there goes that human with that fantastic style
Don't just stand there
Don't just think
Follow your human instinct
Be what you can be
Do what you can do
Celebrate life for all that is true
Show what you can see
And see what you can show
So much can happen
So much can be done
But only you can
No one else
None
The day you die
All you should say is
Thank God
I lived my life the right way
The way it was meant to be
Not the way these magazines and celebrities say or see
But the way my heart feels
But now I am grateful for life

Grateful for these moments
In which I have lived
This world it's everlasting
Eternal events
Nothing can be forgotten
No history bent
Today I stand tall and proud
To say I lived the life of Humilitas
That which I vowed.

Zahra Shareef (13)
Al-Sadiq And Al-Zahra Schools, London

Feelings In Me

I am honest
I express my emotions
I'm always confused about what I should be
Emotions are what I feel
Can I be free?
Being honest is who I am
Kindness and emotion is the best
I'm silent as can be
Being Castitas is what I am
Will I be good? Will I be fair?
Yes, that's me.

Asal Shahrestani (12)
Al-Sadiq And Al-Zahra Schools, London

I Am Humilitas

I've been taught to celebrate what I enjoy
Books, books, books, books,
That's what brings me joy.

My book nook is where it all starts,
All the magic,
Broken hearts,
Tragic stories,
Frozen tarts.

New world,
New places,
Cities cold,
Beautiful oasis.

Wizards, witches,
Tributes and more,
Blizzards, factions
And that's not all.

Unicorns, flying pig,
That's only where it begins.
Hundred Acre woods, the ring,
And more.

Dead or alive,
You'll have to read on,
So dive into one
And let the magic begin.

Myriam Abad (13)
Al-Sadiq And Al-Zahra Schools, London

I Wish They Would Go . . .

I feel isolated and alone,
They never leave me alone,
They're always there,
I wish they would go.

They are evil and cruel,
They don't know what's it like to always feel fear,
I wish they would go.

What's so different about me?
I always feel unwanted and vulnerable, please make it stop,
I wish they would go.

I don't like being in fear all the time,
I'm always scared and I wish I could press a panic button and it would end,
I wish they would go.

Iqra Qureshi
Ayesha Siddiqa Girls School, Southall

No One Should Have No One

No one to say good morning to
No one to bless you when you sneeze
No one to share tea with or coffee for that matter
No one on the end of the phone
No one to share anything with, a cake,
A laugh or a problem
No one to make any day different from the past
No one to turn to when in need
No one should have no one.

Savera Ali (11)
Ayesha Siddiqa Girls School, Southall

You And Your Knowledge

The mistakes you've made today . . .
Are nothing tomorrow
The gains you've gained today
Are not valued tomorrow
However the knowledge you've gained today . . .
Is valued tomorrow
For knowledge will set you free from these iron shackles
Others may boast of their knowledge
But when time catches up with them they die an agonising death
While you die a peaceful death
However, remember, knowledge will set you free . . .

Veranja Jayasundera (12)
Canons High School, Edgware

It's hard to live without you but you know that,
I love teddies only because you're one of them,
You know that I'm the best of all,
You're the bullet, I'm the gun,
We can shoot every problem together.
I'll be with you till the very end,
Those tears will wash away
'Cause I'm your best friend.

Alisha Rathod (11)
Canons High School, Edgware

Slaves Of Pain

Here they stand with their arms around and pray for help
Here they stand with their hands freezing cold as time goes old
No one cares.

It is read upon their faces, the deep scars leaving marks and see from their mind
They have no words left.
They listen to each other's soul escape
When they speak in a lonely low voice as though their spirit was washed away.

They care about what is wasted but don't dare to do a thing
They cry with their eyes open and blink to the scream of help
Another day is wasted and they haven't changed a thing.

Trapped in a cave
Entertain, like slaves of pain.
They rush the miles of hope.
But is there any escape?
The ones hated, are only tyrants of politics building their own statistics.
And them, the poor ones
All they want to do is be peaceful
This means; no death . . . no kill . . . no more thrill!
But in order to survive:
They need to fight!
They want to live!
They should choose what is right.
All I want to say, once and for all, there should be no more war!

Sanziana Cassandra Fanea (15)
Canons High School, Edgware

 # Happy Sun - Haiku

When I see you smile
You really brighten my day
It blows me away.

Candace Dupuis (11)
Canons High School, Edgware

Isn't It Amazing?

Is it always going to feel like this?
As if falling is the only direction
I am my own distraction.

They say it's just a phase
But it feels like a never-ending maze
And in the journey of ups and downs
There are the most confusing voices saying . . .
You're making the wrong choices.

Isn't it amazing
How much a smile can hide?
Such feelings and emotions
Trapped behind my mind.

I can see them every second of every day
Sadness is the beast
Drowning my every plea
Like a cat stuck high up on a tree
But with no fireman to save its grief.

Like never-ending rain
With no ray of sunshine
Causing hopeless pain.

Drip-drop
The sound of my tears
An endless storm
With no land near.

The tears soothe my pain
Like a painkiller
With temporary sustain.

What I have learnt is
Life is like a roundabout
Sometimes you take the wrong way
But don't be led astray
Because in the end everything will be okay.

Sahar Yakin (14)
Capital City Academy, London

There Was A World . . .

There was a world
Full of guns,
Death, destruction,
No peace.

Salute like those
Who fought for us,
Who lived for them,
Who carried on for us.

There was a world
Where bombs were friends,
But also enemies
Who wiped out enemies.

Take a moment for those
Who rose for us,
Who lived for them,
Who killed for us.

There was a world
Where no one was safe,
Had no home,
Had no hope.

Make peace for those
Who risked their lives for us,
Who killed for them,
Who killed for us.

There was a world
Where families were proud,
But also upset,
Lost.

Take pride for those
Who made peace for us,
Who lived for them,
Who protested for us.

There was a world
Filled with slaughter,
But really slowly
We rose and soared.

Remember those
Who spoke for us,
Who lived for them,
Who lived for us.

There was a world
Where there was a ray of hope,
All because of
Our soldiers.

Roshni Bohra (12)
Capital City Academy, London

 # A Tramp

Look at him, a tramp
No life, no home, only a dog
Look at him, a tramp
Begging for food, water and money.

Look at him, a tramp
What had happened to him?
Look at him, a tramp
He had had enough.
Look at him, a tramp
Why was it him that society turned against?

Why me out of all people?
Look at him, a tramp.
No life, but a home full of greed
And wanting more than more.

Look at me
Don't share, don't give
Look at me, just look at me.

Zakaria Berjaoui (12)
Capital City Academy, London

A Positive Side Of Life

All around,
Up and down,
Filled with beautiful thought and sound,
Left and right,
Day and night,
Free from sadness or fright,
Under and over,
Dandelions and clovers,
Down the hills we roll over,
Feeling free,
As we can be,
Life for us is deeply happy,
Grateful,
Not hateful,
This is the life we live for.

Sheyan Seaton (13)
Capital City Academy, London

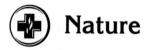

Nature

As summer's warmth dissipates
And the brisk bitterness of the wind appears,
Autumnal spirits congregate
And the leaves fall like tears.

Through each tree nature dwells
And the wild momentum of life slows,
As winter's grasp subtly swells
And nature is evoked as the crisp breeze blows.

Then the flora and fauna blossom and bloom
And the humble Earth's soil is sweetened with dew,
Fruits ripen, harvests boom,
Spring colours in glorious hue.

Sonal Bhundia (13)
Capital City Academy, London

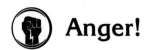 # Anger!

Fire burning inside your flesh
Uncontrollable fury
Cursing the enemy's death.

I tried to help you in life
Now I'm living with flashbacks
And dishonest strife
Left alone, no one to hear, just me
And my fumes zooming out my ears.

My head bursting
Like Chinese New Year.
Do you think this is normal
For a person who does not care?

Noor Salman Alkhuzaiee (12) & Narges (13)
Capital City Academy, London

 # Blizzards

Terrifying, tormenting and tranquillising,
Scaring the life out of innocent children.
Tormenting the unfortunate civilians.
Peaceful.
Playful.
Cloaking the world's flaws.
Draped over the standard ground.
Turning every common home into the White House,
Hiding the rusty copper of the Statue of Liberty.

Erma Xhamaqi (13)
Capital City Academy, London

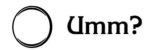

Umm?

Will I finish the poem?
No!
How long will I sit here?
Thoughts stirring, can't get out.
Continuous lines,
Must stay awake,
Too late.

Jessica Bossom (12)
Capital City Academy, London

 # Nelson Mandela

Nelson Mandela was born in July,
He is the man on whom to rely.
He died in December,
That's the most saddest moment we need to remember,
He completely has the right,
To put a worthy fight,
Every black person was separated from white,
But everything changed overnight,
He spent 27 years in prison with no care,
In our hearts he is resident,
So everyone voted for him to be the president.

Prionti Das (11)
Connaught School For Girls, London

I Am Death

The screams
The shouts
The fear
No more

I am death
I cause the fear
I hide the pain
And then you hear . . .
No more!

Watching, waiting,
Tap, tap
I knock
Upon the door
Fresh meat for me!
I am Death!

I make you breathe your last
I cause the sickness
To make you rasp your words
'I am Death,' I shout in glee
'I am Death, yeah that's me.'

Footsteps on the stairs
A twisty handle
Your time has come
Shh! Don't scream!
It's only me!

Megan Hart (11)
Connaught School For Girls, London

A Wave Of Nostalgia; A Fire Of Affection

I want to create something mellifluous,
I wish to murmur it on a starlit night.
I hope to speak it with eloquence,
To redesign, to use initiative,
For the separation of acres to bring us together,
To hear the ocean crashing against the shore,
With the sunset glistening above our heads,
For the moon and the stars to collide,
Creating magnificent, bountiful galaxies.
A wave of nostalgia.
A fire of affection.
As I turn to face you
With our hearts beating in sync.
Perspective.

As I sleep
Melodious harmonies surround me,
Words escaping her lips,
Breathtaking, heart-trembling,
Deep meaning art to my ears.
I figured she didn't want me to hear.
Between these intervals of time
You, my beloved, bring me light.
My heart's desire beside me,
With our hearts syncing to one.

Aamirah Ismail (14)
Connaught School For Girls, London

 # Invincible

I remember it from my past
Its haunting presence always with me.
I remember
The debates,
The choices,
Should my sanity
Or the fear
Take control over me?
I remember . . .

It's back now
Staring me down.
Judging me,
Judging my soul,
Judging my mind,
My achievement, my goals.

I know
It's laughing at me,
It says it knows me,
It says I will never change,
I know
But
Should I be scared of it?
Should I be embarrassed?

No.
The weak will run from it,
The strong will welcome it graciously.
The past made me who I am today.
I am not that person anymore . . .

I am unbreakable,
I am unbeatable,
I am invincible.

I remember I cried
Every time it crossed my mind
My soul sinking in a sea of sorrow.
Slowly
Drowning.
Unable to breathe.

I remember . . .

My soul,
Longing to be free
From the infectious poison
Immobilising me
Now
I'm breaking out
From this chamber of doubt.
Get ready for me
Because I am not what I seem.

I am unbreakable,
I am unbeatable,
I am invincible.

Want a shot at me?
Go ahead, pull the trigger.
If that fear
Strikes through my heart,
Don't think that I will fall.
The fear won't immobilise me,
But will make me strive harder.
So go ahead, fire.
Challenge me,
Isn't that what you desire?

I am unbreakable,
I am unbeatable,
I am
Invincible.

Alima Begum (13)
Elizabeth Garrett Anderson Language College For Girls, London

Me And Them

Honesty is what you ask of me Castitas
Life is the same-old, same-old
Repeating itself day by day
Being a teenager is confusing
One minute you're happy, another snappy

They are me, I am them
Judge me all you like
Dissimilis - different
A. Bit. Of. All.

Temperantia - you ask to reveal my anger
Anger fills my heart and soul
Anger is the thoughts in my head
Anger leads to things I dread
Not allowing me to think ahead

They are me, I am them
Label me all you like
Dissimilis - different
A. Bit. Of. All.

Humilitas - you ask of celebration
Well, here it goes
Ode to my bed
Ode to the colour red
Ode to the food we eat
Ode to the music which makes us complete.

They are me, I am them
Evaluate me all you like
Dissimilis - different
A. Bit. Of. All.

To express my love and emotion Benevolentia you ask
I love my family, who teach me right from wrong
I love my friends who help me be so strong
I hate it when my family and I debate
I hate it when my friends are late.

They are me, I am them
Brand me all you like
Dissimilis - different

A. Bit. Of. All.

You ask - Industria - for diligence
Life is full of brilliance
Each day with something unexpected
Make mistakes - then be corrected.

They are me, I am them
Categorise me all you like
Dissimilis - different
A. Bit. Of. All.

Unique each of us is
A faction I do not fit
A bit of every faction I am
And that's what makes me Dissimilis!

Dea Bozhani (13)
Elizabeth Garrett Anderson Language College For Girls, London

 # Peregrine Falcon

The peregrine falcon is a sneaky sniper waiting for its trigger to be released,
As it soars menacingly high up in the sky,
Its telescopic eyes eagerly search for its helpless victim,
At a distant glance, it shoots through the air,
Giving no mercy on what it sees,
The sniper pierces through its flesh and the shrill cry of the victim is no more,
After devouring this innocent carcass,
It leaves its bones to decay and shoots back into the sky ready to tear through
its next victim.

Alex Arulanantharajah (11)
Enfield Grammar School Upper, Enfield

 # Puberty

I've tried practically all of my days
to be better and better but it never does pay
off or help me to achieve my goals
to be greater and cater to the calls of my soul
but the fire that burns so deep underneath
is fading and changing, buried beneath
the calls of my heart which I cannot resist
and pains in the body no doctor can assist
all this made worse by that fact that I
and all of my peers cannot coexist
and the thorns that have scratched me
and then walls in my way
are all a by-product of mindless decay
of my brain as it falls into endless decay
of my soul as it falls into endless decay.
And I pray that with no further delay
the brain in my heart will go back to the day
where it had no recollection of the beauty and cruelty
of the force of nature that we deem puberty.

Pierre Hamenya (15)
Enfield Grammar School Upper, Enfield

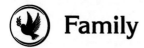 # Family

I love my family more than the world,
They make me happy even when I'm down.
No matter what they tend to make sure that I don't frown,
My sisters and me are so alike,
And one of them works in Nike.
My brother is in Korea for two years,
But now he is gone
I feel like he has disappeared.
I love my family more than anything.

Madi Grace Osborn (13)
Goffs School, Waltham Cross

Never Be Too Late

A sea full of depression
Riddled with aggression,
Sensitive, not sweet,
With nobody left to meet!

Left lonely,
Like a puddle of despair,
Raindrops of tears filling the air,
Yet she runs around the world
With snakes in her hair,
Acting like she doesn't care,
But it is actually a weight pulling her down,
The outside world is a fish tank
And she is beginning to drown!

They hold the key to her heart,
But all she wants to do is part,
Her heart wants to shut them out,
But they have the key,
She has no voice to shout,
So how can she be free?

Holding the knife in her hand,
Feeling ever so grand,
She drops it on the floor
And says, 'I won't take anymore.'
She runs to find someone to tell,
Before she begins to scream and yell,
She picks up the knife again and says, 'This is the end.'

Yasmine Abdelmoula (12)
Goffs School, Waltham Cross

Smile, Because You Can

Smile because God loves you.
No, smile because you love you.
Smile because everyone loves you.
Smile because you're happy.
Smile because you can . . .

Live life to the full
Even when it seems dull and cruel.
When the simple smile fades into a frown
Put on a simple show and turn it around.

Smile because God loves you.
No, smile because you love you.
Smile, because everyone loves you.
Smile because you're happy.
Smile because you can . . .

Take a breath; count to ten,
If it doesn't work, try again.
Joke with joy and live for laughs,
Don't worry about amazing figures or fat calves.

Smile because God loves you.
Smile because you love you.
Smile because everyone loves you.
Smile because you're happy.
Smile because you can . . .

Smile because you're perfect . . .

Maisie Mizon (12)
Goffs School, Waltham Cross

 # I Feel Blessed

As I go through this journey of life -
I feel blessed in the knowledge that I am loved by the love I show others.

Every day, from the moment I wake up
I know there is someone out there that loves me
But also that I can show I care.

Wherever you are - whatever you have or have not -
Remember that only you can make you happy
But I am here to make you smile.

For every good thing we do or every good thought we have
Is what makes our hearts grow stronger -
So remember to smile and make others happy
So that you have a strong heart and a big smile.

There are so many great things in life that make us happy like . . .

Sunshine, raindrops, snowflakes,
The blanket of stars in the night sky,
The sea, the mountains, butterflies, flowers, dancing, music,
Footprints in the sand and so much more,
But I know that when I get that feeling of déjà vu
Or see a floating white feather
I know that my angel is always at my side.

Even on your saddest days remember something that made you smile
So that your heart can get stronger to get you through every day.

If that is me and I made you smile then remember me always smiling . . .

Nadia McCabe
Goffs School, Waltham Cross

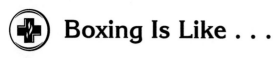

Boxing Is Like . . .

When you step in the arena
It feels like you are a warrior in a chamber of lions.
Fighting, brawling to win the trophy
And claim victory

They scratch and bite and throw you around
Like a rag doll and then you suddenly
Don't hear anything
It's like tunnel vision.

You realise you can win, you can beat them.
You know their weaknesses
You know that they are crumbling like a cookie
You know that!

And then it all stops

The judges have made their decisions
The tension is near
You close your eyes and then the referee pulls your hand up
Your eyes open

And all relief is inside your body and
You scream with joy and get out the chamber
It is all over
You have won!

Kyle Quinn (12)
Goffs School, Waltham Cross

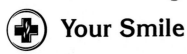

Your Smile

The water trickles through the woods,
A little girl with her books,
She's not as happy as you,
Even the stars look up to you
With the faces shining
And sparkling
Waiting for you to smile.

Your love could power a thousand rockets
As they set off in search of your smile.
Your smile symbolises everything good,
It makes the sun burst through the clouds
And Pluto feels warm.

Your smile makes people feel happy
Even in the darkest times
And it makes the girl in the woods
Put down her books
And smile just like you.
Your smile makes you confident
Your smile makes you happy
Your smile makes you who you are
So keep on smiling.

Molly Pitt (12)
Goffs School, Waltham Cross

 # Fishing

Fishing is my life
But if you go too much you won't have a wife.
I go fishing every weekend
But when I have to go home I don't want the session to end.
When you get that big whopper in your hand
You really do feel grand.

Louie Holmes (12)
Goffs School, Waltham Cross

The Clouds Above

The clouds above, they fly so high,
Like giant birdies in the sky,
They float like the dead sea's ships
And rain down little chips.

The clouds above, they look so soft,
Like my baby teddies in the loft,
They look down towards the Earth,
Watching from our day of birth.

I love the clouds from up above,
They make small pictures of pure white doves,
They make me laugh and jump with glee,
They make me smile like a busy little bee.

I like to think they are made of candyfloss,
Because of their sparkly white gloss,
I know I can't eat the clouds,
But watching the clouds makes me proud.

The clouds above they make me smile,
They make me want to trek the Nile,
I love the clouds from up above,
They make me feel like a floating dove.

Skye Plester (13)
Goffs School, Waltham Cross

 # Shots Fired

It only takes a few words from a person's mouth
To tip me over the edge.
Insults thrown at me daily,
Stay strong that's all they ever told me.
I'm like a champagne bottle,
One more nudge and I'm done.

James Davis
Goffs School, Waltham Cross

I Hate Homework

I hate homework and so should you,
Because it's boring and not very good,
We do enough work at school,
So we don't need it at all,
Now I feel like punching a wall!

Again and again,
I have no pen,
Now I will regret,
Having a debt.
Now my homework is due,
On Tuesday too,
What am I going to do?

As I walk in the room,
I enter my doom,
I speak to the teacher,
Who's like an angry creature.

Then I realise
As I'm about to cry,
That it is due in next Tuesday!

Marcello James Vaccaro (12)
Goffs School, Waltham Cross

Birthday

B irthday day today, yippee!
I am feeling full of glee!
R emembering all the years that have gone by.
T ime to celebrate and party all day and all night.
H aving lots of fun, fun, fun.
D rinks and food for everyone.
A ll these presents just for me.
Y et all I want is for all to be happy.

Joshua Manning
Goffs School, Waltham Cross

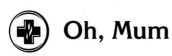 Oh, Mum

M is for Mum
U is for unique
M is for the memories that we will keep

You are as precious as a primrose,
As bright as the sun,
You are as gentle as the wind,
With you I have fun,
You are special in every way,
When I am sad you make my day,
I class you as a best friend
Even though I drive you round the bend.

Mum, you're the best,
I don't even have to test,
You're the strongest in the heart,
I wouldn't want us to be torn apart,
Sometimes we have our ups and downs
And have a boxing round,
But all I want to say,
Is 'I love you'.

Paige Gentle (13)
Goffs School, Waltham Cross

 My Lifelong Dream

We celebrate and party, the world seems a much better place,
I've achieved my lifelong ambition, just to win this one race,
And it's difficult to explain, sometimes I can't describe how I feel,
At last I have done it yet it feels so surreal.
And for no reason at all it sometimes pricks my subconscious state,
A fleeting moment of no importance, will leave me feeling great,
Older times I stare at the trophy, seeing great drivers, names from the past,
I feel tremendous pride to be amongst them, to be world champion!

Charles George Guinchard (13)
Goffs School, Waltham Cross

Mondays

Waking up on that Monday,
It's not going to be a fun day.
Got to go to school at eight thirty in the morning.
I look outside, it's raining, it's pouring.

Even though I'm now in Year 8,
School still isn't great.
It's getting even worse,
As I go along this verse.

I go to see my mates,
As I've just come through the gates.
I ask, 'What lesson have we got?'
They say, 'PE,' and I drop.
I say, 'Oh no, I forgot my kit
And I'm about to have a fit.'

I'm sitting in my det'
And I'm feeling really upset.
Now it is the end you see
And I know they might suspend me.

Francesco Orlando (12)
Goffs School, Waltham Cross

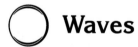 # Waves

The waves crash against the shore
The people want it no more.
Time and time again the deadly dragon destroys all.
The mayor, fat and round
Chooses a sacrifice, a man to take the fall.
The man falls to death
And the waves crash against the shore.
The waves want more.

Patrick Jackson (12)
Goffs School, Waltham Cross

Twinkle, Twinkle Little Star

Twinkle, twinkle little star!
You don't know how special you are!
You light the sky up above
And you fly just like a dove.

You just walked on ahead of us
And we have just got to understand
You must release the ones you love!

We let go of their hands
And we try to cope
But it's hard as we miss you so much!

Your smile and laughter is what we all treasure,
If we only had the moment of pleasure!

Lucky we are that you were sent from Heaven
To fill our lives with love and passion.

We long for your visit from Heaven,
Show us a sign that you are always with us,
One feel, one touch from your safe haven.

Sami Moutawafiq
Goffs School, Waltham Cross

Natures

Thin waves,
The lovely flora,
All perfectly stood,
Very vibrant,
Very admirable,
Ready for beauty to come inside.

Tijen Tekniker (12)
Goffs School, Waltham Cross

My Piano

My piano, my piano,
You can play a smooth song,
My piano, my piano,
You can play a love song.

My piano, my piano,
With your beautiful voice,
My piano, my piano,
You are my only choice.

My piano, my piano,
You're the song in my head,
My piano, my piano,
You play the music I have read.

My piano, my piano,
You are my best friend,
My piano, my piano
Our love will never end!

My piano, my sweet piano . . .

Aiden Mustafa (13)
Goffs School, Waltham Cross

Taken

In the town of Baga people fled
But as they ran they were shot with lead
Boko Haram hunted them down
Destroying everyone who lived in the town
2,000 people lay dead
They went to sleep on Heaven's bed
Given up counting bodies lying on the streets
Communications disrupted, families deplete
This has been described as the group's deadliest massacre
Such tragic news, what a disaster!

Aston Bush (11)
Goffs School, Waltham Cross

Racism Needs To Stop

Racism needs to stop
Martin Luther King gave them rights
Rosa Parks didn't move
Martin Luther King had a dream
Rosa Parks had a dream
Racism needs to stop

Racism needs to stop
Barack Obama is the first black US President
Nelson Mandela served his time for them
Barack Obama had a dream
Nelson Mandela had a dream
Racism needs to stop

Racism needs to stop
And we can do it together
If we all dream
Together we can beat *racism*
Racism needs to stop.

Charlie Tanner (13)
Goffs School, Waltham Cross

Love And Emotion

Love and emotion
A bit like a potion
There's no way out of it
Sit beneath the stars
With someone and your cars
Tell them you love them
Flatter their heart
Sit with your hot dogs
On maybe a water log
Watching lovely films in a park
Probably at 10 or let's just say after dark.

Esin Celebi (13)
Goffs School, Waltham Cross

Summer

Dear Summer,
How I love your blistering days
And warm, wonderful nights.
The taste of your air is sweet like chocolate.
The most amazing feeling is your burning sun
Just gently kissing my shoulders.
Lightening my hair and oh, that gorgeous brown skin.

Bikini, sun dress, and I'm on my way.
The delicious smell of your suncream
Smeared all across my face.
Your fire-hot afternoons
Give me a reason to be lazy and lounge.
Snuggling into the sand of your flawless beaches.
Running fearlessly into your shimmering ocean.
Tan skin, late nights, hot sun, loving life.
How I love you, Summer.
You get me through the rest of the year.

Abigail Smith (13)
Goffs School, Waltham Cross

 # Strictness

Strictness is here to stay,
We don't get our own way,
Teachers dish it out,
All we want to do is shout.

Rules are there to be broken,
But the teacher has spoken,
Strictness is what it's about,
All we want to do is shout.

Learning should be fun,
I'd rather be sitting in the sun,
Rules are bellowed about,
All we want to do is shout.

Exams are on their way,
No time for fun or play.
Good results give me doubt,
All we want to do is shout.

Ryan Hardwick (11)
Goffs School, Waltham Cross

 # Just Take It Easy

If you feel the anger welling up,
And your mind's about to blow.
Just take it out on an object near,
And let your anger go.

If you're getting annoyed in class,
And the teacher tells off you.
Just try and calm yourself down,
And do what you have to do.

If you can't contain yourself anymore
And you don't have a stress ball
Just try and keep it in for longer
And please don't start a brawl.

If you're getting more and more annoyed
And you need a little time out
Just try your hardest not to blow
And definitely don't give a clout.

Jack Aaron Coleman (12)
Goffs School, Waltham Cross

Cancer Can Go

You are a coward,
You are a pain,
You can go, Cancer,
I never want to hear of you again.

I heard of you once
And now you've taken something away,
That something was mine
And you will pay for this one day.

I hate you, Cancer,
You make me sick,
That you've targeted a loved one
And I want to give you such a kick.

We will beat you, Cancer,
So you better watch out,
Because we are coming for you
And we will get you no doubt.

Alexandra Hutchins
Goffs School, Waltham Cross

Final Countdown

Goal! Goal! Goal! Goal! Goal!
Everyone's nerves are rising
Thank God we scored, the game's getting dull
But all the players are trying

I'm on the edge of my seat
And all I see is red
If we win it will be a treat
But if we don't I'm dead

I made a bet with my friend
For a packet of Chewits
They just scored, this is the end
I'm really annoyed that I blew it

There's three minutes of extra time
Sterling's running down the wing
As Liverpool try to reach their prime
We just scored, I need to sing.

Daniel Thomas (13)
Goffs School, Waltham Cross

 # The Countdown

My face is going red,
Something is spinning in my head,
Frightened of the thing I'm going to dread,
I count to ten,
Cooling down,
Turning my frown upside down.

Jason Achilles (12)
Goffs School, Waltham Cross

There's Nothing I Can Do

Awoken by shouts,
There's nothing I can do.
I'm as quiet as a mouse,
There's nothing I can do.

They scream abuse,
There's nothing I can do.
I pray for a truce,
There's nothing I can do.

My family's falling apart,
There's nothing I can do.
It's breaking my heart,
There's nothing I can do.

So I sit and cry,
And try not to make myself die,
But there's nothing I can do.

Kim Edgley (13)
Goffs School, Waltham Cross

Worthless

She picked up the blade
She looked in the mirror
She pictured an image
It couldn't be clearer
She gazed at her eyes
Looked up and down
Glimpsed at her lips . . .
It was a frown

She counted to ten
Then took a deep breath
Then wondered why
People didn't want her to die.

Ceren Koyupinar
Goffs School, Waltham Cross

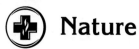 **Nature**

Nature is pure, around us every day
Nature is pretty with flowers on their way.
Nature can be messy, but good and worthwhile.

Bringing me relaxation and tranquillity as my hair floats in the breeze,
Bringing me tears down my cheeks
As the rain falls down on me.

Nature is strong and brave,
With its heavy, ghastly winds.
Nature is a home to all the animals.
Nature is special and one of a kind.
When I open my eyes to look outside I will smile a big smile at nature so kind.
It's free, it's wild, it's fun, it's great, it's pretty, it's pure,
It can be even more.
It's nature, the outside, the place that's always there.
Nature is beyond compare.

Megan Lindop
Goffs School, Waltham Cross

 **Cancer**

You're the victim,
They are the killer,
No one can stop the disease,
It's a traumatic change in your life,
It's life-threatening,
It's a dreadful illness,
You need courage,
It is a monster,
It's hard to remove,
It can be caught anywhere,
It's an awful experience,
Your body tries to fight back the bad cells,
It's always a battle against cancer.

Katherine Smith (12)
Goffs School, Waltham Cross

Because Of The Cyberbully

Cut
Sliced
Sadness mixed with anger
Angry parents tried to find the reason
Her death was always a mystery to everyone.

Confused
Everyone is
Strangled with thoughts
Old razor blades found under her bed
Her death was always a mystery to everyone.

Pale
Cold and dead
It's irreversible
Did she make this mistake or not?
Her death was always a mystery to everyone.

Danni Lethbridge (13)
Goffs School, Waltham Cross

 # Ebola

Ebola cries help everywhere
It's always a complete nightmare
Healthcare worker is now in care
Do you really think this is fair?

People are dying 'cause of this
Where is the crucial missing piece?
We need to find the medicine
So we can help our skeletons.

Ebola is going to spread
People are going to drop dead
We all need to come together
It has to be now or never!

Mickie Linda Jamie Palfreman
Goffs School, Waltham Cross

No!

I guess I get angry easily
Like, I hate when people don't listen to me.
I also don't like it when people shout at me.
I feel that shouting is unnecessary.

If you're rude to me, I'll be rude back.
That's how I am, just like that.
I hate the fact people think they can chat,
About me behind my back.

Bossy people also make me mad.
They boss you around like you've done something bad.
But then lazy people really make me rave.
They can't be bothered so now I'm the slave?

No!

Vida Hood
Goffs School, Waltham Cross

 # 2015 Election

In May 2015 adults across the nation
Will turn up and vote at their polling station.

They will be voting in the next election
Voting for a leader, making their selection.

Who will end up in charge?
Will it be Cameron, Miliband or Farage?

Our country has had many problems for quite a long time
NHS, immigration, deficit and crime.

Who will look after our country the best?
Vote for that one and forget the rest.

Who will be given all the power?
It will be decided at the final hour.

James Martin
Goffs School, Waltham Cross

Eating Cake!

Eating cake, eating cake
How I miss you lovely cake
Eating for breakfast, eating for lunch
Delicious for dinner, more the merrier
Different cake, different day
Black forest Friday
White forest Monday
Three-tier Tuesday
Four-tier Thursday
White chocolate Wednesday
Milk chocolate Saturday
Rainbow cake Sunday
Lovely cake, lovely cake
How I miss you lovely cake.

Niral Shah
Goffs School, Waltham Cross

Chicken Drumsticks

I sit in my chair,
Smelling the amazing smell,
Sizzling and crackling is what I can hear,
It's like an erupting volcano.

My mum moves the pan, making the smell tastier,
It smells beautiful,
Crispy, tasty and mouth-watering,
I saw it in all its glory.

I got ready,
I ran back to my seat ready,
I saw the beautiful chicken drumsticks,
As she brought them in,
I dug in.

Max Sheridan (13)
Goffs School, Waltham Cross

 # Child Labour!

Why should we suffer?
Why should we pay?
Why should we do this every day?
Stop child labour.

Our cuts and bruises aren't healing,
As we do this day by day
And aren't bothered at what we say,
We are tired of doing this every day,
Stop child labour.

So what we're saying is not just a noise,
If you had a heart,
You'd hear a voice
And stop child labour.

Eren Ali Kalayci (13)
Goffs School, Waltham Cross

 # To Mum

Oh Mum,
How beautiful you are,
Your love and affection shows you care,
You feel for me every single day,
You make me shine in the worst moments of my life.

Oh Mum,
You work so hard every single day,
So you keep me alive,
You are my love even if things tear us apart,
Nothing can compare to you,
Your beauty shows your inner perfection,
Your eyes glisten like jewels,
You are my number one.

Oliver Bayliss
Goffs School, Waltham Cross

Untitled

I walked into the food court,
And a fight broke out between two Year 9s.
Kids of all sorts,
Were running for their lives.

I didn't know why,
Until I saw
A terrifying knife,
Right there on the floor.

I was paralysed with shock,
Until Miss Garner rolled up.
I kept on looking at my sock,
And she said, 'Cheer up pup!'

Jason Ludlow (13)
Goffs School, Waltham Cross

Being Me

Nobody knows what it's like to be me,
Except me.
Being me is like winning the lottery,
It's like setting fire to the things you hate with no punishment,
It's like growing up as a young celebrity with no attention,
It's like being picked for what you love all the time,
It's like taking a shot in a sport and never missing.

Nobody knows what it's like to be me,
It's like wanting something that you can't get,
It's like spending money on something that you end up hating,
It's like doing something bad and instantly being caught,
It's a mixture of things, I love being me.

Benjamin Matthew Harris (12)
Goffs School, Waltham Cross

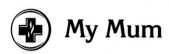

My Mum

When my mum talks to me I'm sometimes in a grump,
But my mum doesn't mind, she knows I've got the hump,
Later on we will normally make up,
And if I'm in a grump again she just tells me to shut up,
My mum always does so much for me,
In return I like to make her tea,
I love her really and she loves me,
That is because we are family,
I need to repay her for all the things she has done for me,
A lovely day with the family by the sea,
I promise I will,
As it will give her a thrill.

Jasmine Sexton (12)
Goffs School, Waltham Cross

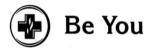

Be You

Be you,
Be true,
Choose to be happy,
Choose to be great.

Don't be sad,
Don't be mad,
Your life is not bad.

Hope is all you need,
You can succeed.
Be you,
Be true.

Sky Merry (12)
Goffs School, Waltham Cross

Sibling Rivalry

My sister gets on my nerves,
She looks at me and observes,
We always fight,
But sometimes it's right.

Sometimes we get along,
But she's always in the wrong,
She can be a pain,
She always thinks she reigns.

She likes to get in the way,
Nearly every day,
But she can also behave.

Abbie Knight (12)
Goffs School, Waltham Cross

The Giant Salamander

Plop! Slop! Squelch! Belch!
Sip! Sap! Boil! Spat!
Slimier than the tapeworm
Peachier than toads
Jabba the Hut junior
Put on weight and loads
Fatter than Big Momma
Sleeps all winter and all summer
The sight is so unholy
That luck was never known
The alien of China's waters
The discovery has been found
His belch is so loud
It takes over the entire world
No one can ever stop him
Godzilla isn't safe and sound
If it ever comes to your door hide your stash of food right now!

Michael Gayle (12)
Greig City Academy, London

Another Me

I'm further than you think I
Maybe,
Isolated, in oneself,
Speaking to me.
An island, I stay waiting
The sun never rising,
I'm a lost soul
Never witnessing hope come by.
I like to think
I'm looking for hope,
But no, I stay, for a thousand years
Wondering if it does exist,
As I stare at the horizon,
Dark as the raven's feather,
And I wait,
I do not pursue, I do not find,
Only aspiring for a human being,
Another me.
I wish for a person's company,
One who thinks like I,
One who would bring happiness
To what's left of my fragile soul,
That's what I'm waiting for,
Another me.
I don't try to look for happiness,
Though I do like to think so,
And I wait,
For hope,
For happiness,
Another me.

Erik Palushi (12)
Greig City Academy, London

 # Life

Life can be boring
Life can be funny
Life can be soft
Like a white bunny

Life can be annoying
Life can be black
Life will make you feel like
Running away in a sack

Life can be hot
Life can be cold
Life might sometimes smell
Like mould

Life can be wet
Life can be dry
Life will sometimes
Make you cry

Life can be hard
Life can be soft
Life will sometimes make you
Feel lost

Life can be red
Just like a rose
But love makes you
Angry when the wind blows.

Tihana Williamson (12)
Greig City Academy, London

Nature In The City

I run through the green fields,
River bubbling happily beside me,
The rushes whispering in sudden gusts,
The scent of flowers filling my nostrils,
I taste the fresh, clean, perfect air,
The soft grass brushing my ankles,
Or,
I sit in my swivel chair,
Watch characters dance across my screen,
Jab at the keyboard and curse,
I would not know there was a thing called a tree,
I would sit between my pillars of steel, concrete and glass oblivious to all
around me,
Or,
Racing through the waves,
Feeling the pull of the wind,
The dunes passing beside me,
The sea spray, sun and rush of adrenalin,
All lost in the bustle of the city,
And yet,
If you look hard enough,
Some patches of green still show,
Some trees standing in a cobbled square,
Small havens,
All is not lost for the world.

Max Hahn
Greig City Academy, London

Saltwater Crocodile

It is the rivers' most feared creature
Even the water is afraid of it.
It is longer than Sideshow Bob's feet
And its back is like sharp, green icicles.

It is the devil beneath the water
And to its prey it is the Hulk.
Lurking silently like a ninja is its hobby
And its teeth are like an alley of knives.

Trust me, it may be beautiful
But once you get to know it,
Snap, snap, crunch, crunch
Will be the noise of your bones at the end.

It camouflages in the dirty, smelly water
And stalks until it gets its lunch.
Giving up won't be an option
It will hunt until it gets its prey.

So never be tempted by its eye-catching looks
Because you could be its meal.
This is the world's most deadly reptile
The one and only saltwater crocodile.

Alvi Islam
Greig City Academy, London

Let Us Be Free

Let us go there, only me and you
The place no one else can see
Where animals can be free
When the stars will rise for us
Where the clouds will lead us
In the place of dreams, only me and you.

Julia Fraszek
Greig City Academy, London

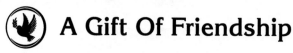 A Gift Of Friendship

Life can be tricky at times
You might not get pennies and dimes
But someday you'll find a friend
Who will be with you till the very end

When there's something
You don't understand
You'll always know
That you have a helping hand

Whenever you're unsure
Don't have doubts
Just go to your friends
They'll help you out

Friendship is a priceless gift
That cannot be sent or sold
But its value is far greater
Than a mountain made of gold

Gold won't bring you adventures
Nor will it stay long with you
But at least you have a friend
Who is always loyal and true.

Shantay Whyte
Greig City Academy, London

 Guilt

G reat as I am
U nlike I have never been before
I look back into the past
L ooking into the mistakes I have done once more
T he guilt I hide will never show.

Keenya Gayle
Greig City Academy, London

Untitled

Life is a roller coaster,
Life is time,
Life is beat,
So spread your wings and fly.

Life is love,
Life is a dove,
Life is an adventure,
An adventure from above.

Life is sad,
Life is torture,
Life is lonely,
So don't let you down.

Life is full of changes,
Full of surprises,
Make your changes,
And live life.

Rebekah Adeniji
Greig City Academy, London

The Crocodile

C reeps out beneath the dirty water
R eluctantly waits for its prey
O bserves the prey before it attacks
C ruelly drowns the victim
O bviously a dangerous amphibian
D evours the food promptly
I n the water it lays
L azily lurking around
E agerly waits for more.

Oshika Guptar
Greig City Academy, London

A Sonnet For Reading

Reading's my undeniable passion,
Books are trees, themes branches, words falling leaves,
The characters are the satisfaction
And the description is like fancy weaves.

The celebrities, fashion magazines,
It's not style that I'm interested in,
But the crime fiction abnormalities,
They're just genres but who are you to pin.

When I read the pages smell like roses,
When I read my mind hurls off to many
Different worlds, but don't judge; I like poses,
Call me bookworm; I don't give a penny.

For make-up and clothes I really don't care,
Painting pictures with words is my fresh air.

Nailaa Islam-Bint Hosen (12)
Greig City Academy, London

World Of Warcraft

Everyone's happy
Everyone's glad
That they put down their homework
And got out their mouse pad
Ten pounds a month
Is a pretty good price
If it's a wonderful world
With people that are nice
We're spending all night
Playing this game
There's millions of us
So I'll tell you its name
World of Warcraft.

Benedict Whitehead (12)
Greig City Academy, London

Untitled

L eaping, crawling, pouncing onto his prey,
E agerly wanting his prey,
O verlapping blood on his mouth,
P owerful jaws crack the bone,
A s fierce as fire he attacks everything,
R uns as fast as a Lamborghini,
D ashes his prey to the ground,
S neaky little dotted animal.

Silent as a pin drop, powerful as a rock,
Cracks a human's bone
As clever as a human,
Sneaky as a snake,
Ambushes his prey,
Dotted little animal.

Bence Parazso
Greig City Academy, London

Speak Out

A bird is like a spear
Cutting the skies
Just let it grow
Free, so free to the bone
But don't trap it in a cage
Let it grow
Save the little soul
Gazing at the night skies
From over the milky clouds
Closer than any of us but sad, so sad
Right inside in the heart
Because no one spoke out
Because no one liberated
Auschwitz before.

Klaudiusz David Kolodziej (13)
Greig City Academy, London

Sonnet For My Guitar

My darling standing in my room alone,
Leaving her is a heartbreak every day,
To be with you I would break my own bones,
I remember when I bought you in May,
The way you sing is a joy to the ear,
Plucking your vocal chords is like Heaven,
I wish you could be with me over here,
We've been with each other since Year 7,
Together we will both rise to the stars,
We will both be rich and in big glory,
We'll be riding in our expensive cars,
Then we'll be able to tell our story
And by Heaven, our love is truly rare,
No one's love can be to our love compared.

Kacper Frankiewicz
Greig City Academy, London

Pilosaur

From the love I give to animals you are thy mystery I ponder.
What art of creation!
Beauty never wins - it is thy thought which is the answer,
Never be different because you are the anomalous, the vigilante,
The fear that may cause to be thy evil scent you emit,
Have you been created by God or have you been created by Mother Nature?
The knights of King Arthur fade by comparison to your fury
Your eyes of despair
Your teeth of Excalibur's blade,
Your sly body does not meet the eye.
Black and white is only the beauty of thee,
Belief is not a truth if not seen,
From the love I give to animals you are the mystery I ponder.
What art of creation.

Darnéll Amari Rousseau (12)
Greig City Academy, London

Pizza Sonnet

You make me dribble every single day,
Your pepperoni eyes are a delight,
Your bright yellow sweetcorn is a sunray,
I know it is bad but it feels so right.
Your melted cheese is like a bad disease,
Your vivid colours are like a rainbow
When I see you I can feel a huge breeze,
Although your smell drags me down so very low.
My sad eyes seem to pop when I see you,
I feel dizzy when I see your beauty
I feel clueless like I'm out of the blue,
Your ever so pretty face is a cutey
Your name is Pizza, and I am Anna
Nothing compares (except a banana).

Anna Kapanadze
Greig City Academy, London

It's My Life

It's my life, they don't understand. They never have and they never will.
It's those doors, the school doors. That's when it starts.
I walk; I walk into the doors of hell. Where everyone knows my name, where
everyone thinks I'm a monster, I have a life. They don't understand, it's my life.
It wasn't the first time; they used to whisper; now they talk.
They look with disgust, no one likes me. They don't understand what it is like
to be me, it's my life.
They wouldn't last a day, or an hour.
My stomach churns at the thought of them. Then it builds up. The reason I am
a so-called monster but it's my life. Am I not allowed to feel?
They don't know. They never have known.
It's just my life, I am not a monster.
Well, I don't want to be . . .

Harpreet Malli (12)
Harlington Community School, Hayes

My History Poem

History is a mystery,
To you and me,
I'll take you on a journey,
To see what we can see.

Let's talk about the Romans,
Whose emperors lived in villas,
There were giant luxury homes,
Made using mosaics and pillars.

The most famous Roman was Julius Caesar,
He ruled for a long, long time,
He fell in love with Queen Cleopatra,
But was killed while in his prime.

Vikings came in 790AD,
And caused a bit of a stir,
They carried lots of shields and swords,
And their clothes were lined with fur.

On their heads they wore a helmet,
And on each side a horn,
They rampaged through the village,
And crushed down all the corn.

Moving on quite quickly,
We now go to 1491,
A boy was born in England,
And he was an important one.

Henry VIII was who he was,
In his time he had six wives,
Two of them lost their heads,
And only the last survived.

In a hundred years to come,
History will involve us,
From Queen Elizabeth the second,
To the big red London bus.

Alice Baggott (12)
Harlington Community School, Hayes

It Had To Be You

You. It had to be you. I go to sleep . . . I dream about you . . .
I look in the mirror . . .
I see you
I turn on the radio . . .
I hear you!
Why does it have to be you?
When I look at you, I feel dizzy
My eyes burn and my hands shake
It's because I know what you did
And I'll *never* forgive you!
When I hear you I go deaf!
I want to throw this burning world on your face!
I want to scream until all that is left of you is your flesh and bones
When your ghastly soul appears in my thoughts
I want to tear you into pieces
But it had to be you!
What you did was not a joke
What you did was not a mistake
What you did put a dent in my heart forever
I'd rather jump off a cliff than see you
I'd rather be eaten alive than think about you
I'd rather stab myself in the heart than know you're there
Because what you did was not a joke
what you did was not a mistake
What you did put a dent in my heart forever
But it just had to be you.
No one else. Just you.
Murder is not accidental
Betrayal is not a mistake
Torture is not a joke
But it all . . . had to be . . . you.

Ayesha Hafiz (12)
Harlington Community School, Hayes

They Were Wrong

I'm surrounded by people who repeat the rhyme 'sticks and stones'
Well they were wrong
They told me I was ugly
I believed them
I constantly looked at myself in the mirror
Now I know
They were wrong
They told me I would never be normal
I took it to heart and hid in the shadows
Hoping no one would see me
But now I know they were wrong
They called me a freak
I slowly drowned in the rivers of my insecurity
Now I see
They were wrong
Don't tell me these words hurt less than broken bones
I've learnt that
If you see anything beautiful about yourself
Get a mirror
Look a little closer
Stare a little longer
Make sure at least you see your beauty
Because
If you don't see 'They were wrong', nobody will for you.

I will remember these three words for life, They Were Wrong.

Afonama Ntefon (12)
Harlington Community School, Hayes

 # How I Feel

You build up my happiness
When I am feeling sad
You help me fix my injured heart
Whenever I am unhappy.

You're such an amusement in my soul
I hope that you feel the same
How mean your friendship is
You're a total luxury to me.

Thank you for what you've done
this means so much to me
For concern and understanding
You give generously.

Sujan Sareskumar (12)
Harlington Community School, Hayes

 # They're Staring

I was walking, carrying the burden of God's anger,
I was considered an enemy; they think I mean hell for whoever I set eyes on,
God has sent me on a mission; a mission I don't want to be a part of,
A mission to make people's lives a misery.
I stomp viciously into the room until my sight is clear,
There is a whole hall full of them. Too many,
It was not the first time they stared at me like this,
Never in my life had I seen so many eyes of hatred,
They looked as I walked past. I know what they were thinking.
I open the class door. It falls silent. Too silent.
They stare. Their eyes full of disgust.

Amira Haji-Ali (12)
Harlington Community School, Hayes

⚖ Restraint

Restraint
Corporate greed like hungry beasts
Whipped and lashed into silence
Our brains are conditioned
It's an ongoing process of control
How long will we have to believe what's wrong
We are told what to think
What to feel
What to write
What to say
Every last ounce of creativity crammed into a box and locked away
We don't have our own voice
Even though we are told time and time again
That the people have a voice
Where is that voice?
Who is that voice?
We are clasped in the hands of society
Strangled by the hands of law
We fight
We rebel
And we are shot down
Yet we are all shot down . . . as the 'people'
We few, we a small gathering
We are used as examples
Examples to the outside world who take what they're given
Examples to do what we're told
Examples to not rebel against social normality
What is normal or social normality?
That's the thing you cannot define normal
It is our perception of life which is presented
To be normal
Why is it normal to believe one race is good and one race is bad
Why is it normal that one voice is listened to but all the others are silent
Locked in the prison of their imagination and creativity
Restraint.

Jadesola Olusanya (13)
Harris Academy, London

The Rage Of A Slave

Angry as can be,
Confined by the four walls round me,
I once was a free bird,
But now I am contained by this cage.
My feet chained,
I am a slave to humanity,
People think that I can be trained,
Trained like a dog to fetch a toy.
I am trapped and my soul can't be free,
I need to leave but these chains contain me,
Cleaning up after people's mess
Like a mother cleaning up after a two-year-old child.
They call me names,
Laughing as if it's just a game,
The names they call me, it hurts,
I wanna tell someone but I am silenced.
They scream at me,
They torture me,
They kidnapped me,
They torture me.
I want my revenge,
But I am contained,
I want to scream, I want to shout,
But I am silenced.
I cannot act as a normal person,
I am confined, contained and silenced,
Kidnapped, taken away,
Treated like nothing, I am only a slave.
I once could fly,
But never again,
I once could speak my mind,
But now I am silenced.
I am filled with so much rage,
Trapped like a flightless bird,
I am a slave.

Charde Pinnock (13)
Harris Academy, London

⬭ Dissimilis

Enjoy every moment of the day,
And let your problems go away,
Listen to what I have to say.

The trees move side to side,
But I still have pride,
The leaves shrink up and then die.

My head is spinning around,
And I can't figure out what is brown,
However, I can hear a sound.

I wish I wished upon a shooting star,
That I can have a car,
But I want a guitar.

Life is so unfair,
That I can hear the air,
However, why is it so rare?

99% of us,
Are always making a fuss,
When we are taking the bus.

Here is a joke,
What did the kid say to the bloke,
You smell like smoke.

I hate to sing,
But I love spring,
In addition I have rings.

This is all I have to say,
So have a good day,
Goodbye and stay awake.

Theola Jones (12)
Harris Academy, London

I Am Dissimilis

I take the test,
It decided my fate,
To tell me I am Dissimilis
Oh, that's just great.

To choose my own path,
Of what I want to be
Temperantia, Temperantia, Temperantia
That's what my mind says to me.

It's better to love than hate
that's all they say to me
But how can I love someone
Who frustrates the hell out of me?

Your arms are made to hug people, not to hit
you want me to hug that thing
Please give me my plane ticket

I despise that lady, can you not tell?
She only came here to make our lives a living hell

The woman from hell, that is her name
My fists need a punch bag
Hey, why not use your face

You can call me angry, annoyed,
Whatever you please.

But I think it would be a smart idea,
To keep that woman away from me.

So Temperantia is where I belong,
For my hatred on this woman
Has grown so strong.

Maisie-Jane Lewis (14)
Harris Academy, London

The Cage

This bird
Who was once able to fly
The sky is the limit they say
It's not the same for I

Why must these shackles keep me chained to the ground?
I scream and shout but nothing comes out
The walls are closing around me
How can one vent their rage in such a small cage?

The only company I have is the light
Emitting from the outside
It just makes me want to cry!
For I know, I shall never be let outside

My wings have been clipped
I might as well die
For at least then I can be as free as a fly
With only dreams to accompany me
In this claustrophobic room
All I see before me is doom

They only want to use me for their show
I'm a rarity, I know
But everyone else should be treated the same
Do they think that this is a game?

If so, I quit
I'm done with this
I'm sick!
I can't take this anymore
I have crumbled down to the core
There is no use for me anymore.

Malika Ould Mohammed (14)
Harris Academy, London

 # On My Own

6,336 hours since I've touched another human being
6,336 since I realised I could never belong
I ventured carefully, afraid of what they thought of me
If only you understood
If only you could see
What this loneliness was doing to me
I laugh, but inside I'm dying
Trying to fit in but I'm sick of trying
When they see me cry they think that I'm weak
What they don't know is that I've been strong for too long
Mother always said that everyone wants happiness
And nobody wants pain but you can't make a rainbow
Without a little bit of rain
Though where is she now?
I'm sure she's ashamed, I would be too
The highlight of my day is always going to sleep
I never want to wake up
I'll admit that it's sad
Though it feels like I'm having a reverse nightmare
That I woke up to a nightmare
It's not my fault that I don't belong
I always wanted my life to be a song
Something sweet and easy to enjoy
The look of disappointment in their eyes
That's when I knew I'd just pawned off my life
Like some cheap watch that never told the right time
I slit my wrists and cut my thighs
Fake a smile and dry my eyes
Welcome to my beautiful world
My beautiful world of lies.

Asma Bah (13)
Harris Academy, London

Anger Problem

Most people don't know how I feel
Cause I keep it in
Within my heart
With my tears

People don't see
What pain they cause
With their looks
Their tones
And their expressive movements

But you cause my pain
You cause my torture
And you don't know how
And how I break down inside

It all starts with the looks
Then talks
The people ignoring you
People pushing you away
People afraid to be near you

Then it stays inside your minds
And every word someone says
Is recorded in your mind
You feel alone
That's how the anger starts

You hold it in.

Zainab Ibrahim (11)
Harris Academy, London

Stop, Smile And Have Hope

The world is a place full of anguish
Only if you let your demons take over
Yes, there are monsters constantly mutating
Some hidden in the dark, some stand in plain sight
It doesn't mean humanity is lost

Amongst the demons lie angels
Restoring faith into the world
A helping hand always at your call
So before you think all is lost
Stop, smile and have hope

Lurking amongst the shadows; lay your darkest fears
Standing tall and mighty in all its glory, hope
Near or far, wherever you may be, hope is there
So before you think all is lost
Stop, smile and have hope

It may be hard to see the beauty of the world
It's disguised by its demons
But when you peel back the mask of pain
When you slay all your demons
You will witness the beauty of the world

So before you think all is lost
And humanity can't be salvaged
Take a minute and stop
Stop, smile and have hope.

Susan Derby
Harris Academy, London

Untitled

Best friends are hard to find,
But easy to lose.
When trouble comes by,
A friend who stands by,
Will brighten your day because they're
A shining star.

The kindness of two friends is
The key to a happy life.
The real best friends are the ones
Who give you the confidence
To never give up.

Friendship is a priceless gift,
It cannot be bought or sold,
A friend is worth more than
Diamonds, pearls or gold, the
Value is greater than anything
You could think of.

Friends care, friends share and friends
Give hope.
Throughout the good times
And the bad ones
A friend will be there
Like an angel
Ready to be there by your side.

Gulce Yilmaz (11)
Harris Academy, London

Friendship

A friend is someone who understands you,
When the world turns into a nightmare,
As good as an angel,
Especially my friend.

They always be nice to you,
Staying by your side.
Friends don't break your heart,
Because they are nice.

There is no way to thank them,
For everything they do.
No matter where or when,
Always making you smile.

They never leave you behind,
No matter where or when.
They can change your life,
They're your shining star.

They accept your thoughts and feelings,
No matter where or when,
For never giving up,
Being my best friend.

Just to say something to my friend,
Thanks for being my shiny star,
Friendship.

Armeta Ezaz
Harris Academy, London

Love And Emotion

Blush . . .
You always make me blush
That tingling sensation that flows
Throughout my cheeks
As you flatter me with sweet words you speak

Grasp . . .
Your touch; your embrace
They send goosebumps down my spine
So chilling it makes it hard to breathe

You complete me
You make me whole
You're my other half

Love . . .
I will stay with you till the day I die
And be by your side
Because I'm your ride, or die

The only words that come to mind
Are words so commonly used
I want them to be unique to realise everything I feel

To me, they aren't enough but yet they'll have to do

I love you . . .

Najma Ibrahim (14)
Harris Academy, London

 # Betrayal

You give your heart to someone
You give your love
You give your trust
You give your honesty
You give your loyalty
But all you receive is
Hurt
Pain
Shattered dreams
Broken heart
Sorrow
Tears

Trust is earned, respect is given
And loyalty is demonstrated
Betrayal of any one of those is
To lose all three
You cheated on me continuously
You covered up your acts tactfully
You are nothing but a curse on me
That's why I hate you endlessly
I hate you!

Rabiat Garba (14)
Harris Academy, London

So Much To Do, So Little Time To Do It

The stress,
The anxiety,
The tension,
I count the days down,
Always with a frown,
Everywhere I look,
I always see a book,
I can never escape this forever lasting misery.

The stress,
The anxiety,
The tension,
The beat of my heart is racing,
Three, two, one.
When the teachers count down,
It's all about winning the crown,

Let the exams begin!

Klara Molla (14)
Harris Academy, London

Growing Up

Growing up is like fixing broken glass with no glue.
I'm becoming a teenager!
But I don't know what to do.
I live my life with no stress.
But being a teenager is not the best.
I can walk and talk but I wish I was younger.
Well I am now twelve, I'm becoming stronger.
Growing isn't easy when you're small.
I hate to realise I'm growing tall.

Diandra Henry (12)
Harris Academy, London

That's The Past

I'm not normal
I'm different
No one can change me
Even if they try

I've been called names
I've been strangled
I've been through a lot
And I always stay quiet

No one knows me
I'm a mystery
I've been through a lot
It's hard being me

But now my life is different
I love everything around me
My friends and family
Without them I'll be lonely
I wouldn't have anybody.

Tanem Durust (12)
Harris Academy, London

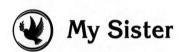 # My Sister

My sister, my sister
She is getting on my nerves
To be fed with Brussels sprouts
That is what she deserves
Every day she is nothing but trouble
Because she will babble and babble
But when I think about it
I have to admit
That really she has got wit
And I love her much more than a bit.

Aisha Momodou Ceesay
Harris Academy, London

Stop Deforestation

Shimmer! Sparkle!
Tiny lights flicker around me,
Ever-changing, never stopping.
They move in unison, yet none are the same!
The shadows they cast dance,
Pooling at my feet or climbing up the trees.
Like liquid, they move freely and with grace.

Yet alas! The moment is broken!
Hulking metal machines which spew smoke screech with anger,
Trampling this sacred ground!
The lights flee!
The shadows disperse!
There is
Nobody left
Except
I.

Lisa Wang (13)
Harris Academy, London

The World

A round sphere as a world domain
Prevailing winds southern over the air in the deep, gloomy sky
People with different minds and sympathy
The world at his greatest feet
Universe, planets and stars
Out in the midnight
They come once in a while every night
Day and night people work and work
Pollution natured out of trees
Flowers beautiful as the fragranced perfume.

Blue cascade through the midst
Animals out for the predator
Cheetah, stealth and stamina
Snow, pure white as luxurious soft pillow
Cold as the breeze.

Rida Alam (13)
Harris Academy, London

Lost Teenager

Silence floating in a sea of
black. I peer into the silvery water
And I see the reflection of a pale
Boy, confused. Painfully young. Who
Doesn't know what he's going to do
With his life. That's me, lost and
Blank.

No one knows what I feel, they
Only hear loud silence.
Trying to escape through
Bad thoughts. Trying to find
Freedom. I am a puzzled
And confused teenager. My mind
Is a labyrinth.

Anna Roberts
Harris Academy, London

Best Friend

You are the ice to my cream
The peanut to my butter
But most importantly you are the best to my friend
You have been here for me since the beginning to end
You are my sister
My human diary
My other half (me/you)
We share the most bizarre things with each other
And I have lived the best part of my life with you
The love I have for her can never be broken
Forever and always princess
We are a team
You mean everything to me
I love you Katie.

Chloe Bates (14)
Harris Academy, London

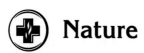 # Nature

Nature, such a wonderful thing
The sound of the birds
Makes me feel like a king
No matter what it is
The birds in the trees
The dogs covered in fleas
Even if it's nature
Over the seas.

The barnacles stuck to the boat
Trapped by the world's largest moat
The underwater caverns
Glisten
With the scales
Of a school of rainbow trout
Even if it's nature in the
Desert.

The pythons
In the sand
While the camels form a band
The scorpions
Jump out
And kill
The lizards without a doubt
No matter what it is.

Whatever it is, a plant, animal, fish, reptile, crustacean
They will be doing what they want on the wonderful planet of Earth.

Sanchez Lagos (11)
Harris Academy Peckham, London

This Kid

This kid likes Call of Duty 2
But that's not the only thing he likes to do
He often watches Doctor Who
But he doesn't like the loo

This kid does not like the clock
This kid doesn't like the sound *tick, tock*
This kid is in shock
Because his phone has a lock

This kid likes school
This proves he's not a fool
He uses his pen as a tool
But he's still cool

He does not like long books
Because of the way they look
But he still took the book
So his mum let him off the hook

This kid's name is Ali
And no, he does not look like Sally
He's not that funny
But it's better when it's sunny

Ali's favourite colour is yellow
Because it rhymes with fellow
Ali is as nice as a cat
This kid sure is the opposite of fat.

Ali Abdulle (12)
Harris Academy Peckham, London

 # Darkness

Anger shall be filled with darkness
Darkness shall be flooded with hate
Hate shall be released with power.

I will hate until my last breath
The rats run and the cats hunt.
Oh how I love the cycle of death
I shall hate thee until my last breath
I shall hate thee to the pitiful hole in my chest.
I am so happy the end is near.

I watch as the flies rot on corpses below me
I can't help but walk near the next graveyard
Next to me, I see all the rotting flowers on
The decayed as the funeral music is played.

I feel emotion coming from my eyes, my eyes
As my heart throbs, as my tears hit the floor
I limp through the alleyway as tears go dry
As though I'm a dog.

Yet the sadness still remains
And I begin to think there must be some
Way to escape this mental fray.
I lie back knowing I won't change.

But my mind is the only thing controlling me
I've created anger because there's nothing left.

Kieran Joshua Cutenar (12)
Harris Academy Peckham, London

 Walking

Walking around,
Up and down,
Just looking around,
Looking at all the dreams,
Looking at all the stars,
Looking at the people,
Who don't have a heart,
Children, just children,
Being children,
But again,
I'm just looking around,
Just walking forward,
Step by step,
Achieving a goal,
That I once,
Set.

Harmony Lony (12)
Harris Academy Peckham, London

 Vallie

Love is what I think about
While exercising through the night
The joy of coming together
Celebrating and trusting each other
Valentines is a day for me
Talking about all the love I receive
Valentines, just one day a year
I am so happy that it is near.

Taiyah Brown (12)
Harris Academy Peckham, London

Breaking The Rules

'Don't chew gum,' my teacher says
I say chew, chew, chew
'Don't swing on your chair,' my teacher says
I say swing, swing, swing
'Don't play games,' my teacher says
I say play, play, play
'Don't shout out,' my teacher says
I say shout, shout, shout
'Don't tap your pencil,' my teacher says
I say tap, tap, tap
'Don't walk around the classroom,' my teacher says
I say walk, walk, walk
'Write a poem,' my teacher says
I write, write, write . . .

Siris Bennett (11)
Harris Academy Peckham, London

 # Love

Love is a feeling like no other
Love is a feeling that makes you wonder
It's like thunder
It will make you stronger
So don't ponder
Or wait until you're older.

Vanesa Gigova (13)
Harris City Academy Crystal Palace, London

The Dove That Helped Our Love

We sat on the park bench,
Looking at the sky.
So many birds,
But two caught our eye.

They were side by side,
Flying gracefully amongst the tree.
'Wow!' I said,
'That could be a resemblance between you and me.'

A beautiful white colour,
It was so gorgeous to see.
The glistening, soft texture.
Their feathers seemed to agree.

In unison they fly,
Like love is in the air.
Soaring through the sky,
Like they don't seem to care.

As a couple we stare at the tree,
Wondering what this amazing bird can be.
Its yellow beak gleams in the sunlight.
No need to perceive.

What to wonder,
What to think.
This stunning creature,
Makes you not want to blink.

We hold hands with each other;
I feel the breeze upon my face.
In the lovely summer weather,
This moment is to embrace.

Somebody tell me what this being is!
Look, a dove! A dove!
A child yells to his miss,
And it's a symbol of peace and love!

Tahera Begum (11)
Harris City Academy Crystal Palace, London

The Shield

The shield
Three brothers
One family
Full aggression
No respect
Just each other
Nobody else
Appreciate each other
Nobody else
The shield

Until the mastermind
The creator
Betrayed us
For evolution
Broke the shield
The formidable team
Crushed by greed
No respect
Ending hope
The broken shield

But now
Two brothers
One family
No holds barred
Disrespect
Just one another
Devolution
Destruction
Applying hope
We're coming

The shield reborn.

Jason Majekodunmi-O'Hara (14)
Harris City Academy Crystal Palace, London

When You're Wrong

There are a few decisions in my life that I have to deal with
Wondering to myself countless times
Left and right, up and down
But the mind is hard to convince
When you're wrong

Lying to myself
When it's staring me right in the face
Trying to avoid it but it's hard
Tried going north
Tried going east
Tried going south
Tried going west
But there's never an escape
When you're wrong

How can I show my emotions?
Trying to get it out, but it doesn't flow
Is it me?
Is it him?
Or, is it the both of us?

But do you know what he'd always say to me?
He would tell me to jump
But I'd say how high?
He would tell me to leap
But I'd say how far?
He would tell me always
But I'd say *never*

Each day he'd say
'Jump high'
'Leap far'
But never say, never
Because there's always something that lies ahead

You know who he is?
It's me
I have been wrong,
I've lied to myself,
But what I've learnt is that it's always best to be true to yourself
Because you can lie to yourself,

But you can never hide from yourself!
When you can admit to yourself that you're wrong,
Only then can you be true to yourself.

Nashada Saka (13)
Harris City Academy Crystal Palace, London

 # Season Of Love

You were an angel given to me,
As a gift from God,
You cared for me and showed me,
The way,
You never let me feel lonely,
I am what I am because
Of you,
You laughed with me,
Cried with me,
You even stare into my eyes;
You have done this before,
You uncover all my emotions,
Secrets,
I never knew I was hiding,
Those moments which I cherish
Stay hidden inside the depths of
My heart.
I love you so much,
I don't even know how to explain it,
The sun will shine,
The rain will pour,
And the snow will fall,
But the season of my heart,
Mind,
And soul,
Will never change.

Camara Bourne (13)
Harris City Academy Crystal Palace, London

The Power Of Earth

As the sirens wailed,
So did the people,
Running, running,
Running to their homes,
Running from fear,
But they will not escape,
Fear is everywhere.

No man can escape,
From this great power,
No one can control it,
No one can survive it,
Make the world shake,
In a great earthquake,
Knock down skyscrapers,
Bury the remainders.

The place we call home,
Is our ruler,
We never know,
What the Earth will do next,
It controls us,
But we fight back.

It thunders its anger,
It shakes its revenge,
It blows its sadness,
People run,
Running, running,
Running to your home,
Running from fear,
But you will not escape,
Because fear is always near.

Finlay Thomas Alcock (11)
Harris City Academy Crystal Palace, London

Charlie Hebdo

Charlie Hebdo were writing a magazine
They were asked to stop or the extremists would intervene
Making fun of all religions, a controversial subject
Is it alright or is it not, lots of people wanted it to stop
These men were extremists
So they wouldn't be classed as Muslims, I'll tell you this
They killed twelve people at Charlie Hebdo
Then went on the run, they thought it was done
But they were wrong
This story is long, so I'm going to stop here
It gets a bit emotional, might bring a tear
The police went on a manhunt round in circles
Like the back of a really large turtle's shell
One of the men handed himself in
He could have just gone and hid in a bin
The two brothers broke into the quarters
Smashing into a room
They all thought this was doom
But in the cupboard there was a man giving information to the police
Saving people's lives at the least
The brothers were surrounded by the police
Un, deux, trois, quatre, cinq, six
Bang! The brothers were down but is this the end of this?
Will there be bliss?

Sadia Kabeya (12)
Harris City Academy Crystal Palace, London

The Beauty Of Life And Death

The beauty of life is like the beauty of death
Without death, you cannot have life
Without life you cannot have death
We were made to live
We were made to die
So wouldn't living be like dying
Or is it the other way around
Would dying be like living?
Or are they exactly the same thing?
What are the differences and similarities between the two?

What if the wind were to cry and the ground were to shake
Wouldn't the balance between the two break?
What if a tree were to crust and die
Or a flower was to wither away?
The start of a new cycle would begin
The seeds would bury themselves underground to grow their roots
Then they would sprout up, out of the ground
They would grow up, up and up until they had reached their end
And die.

Everything has a meaning to live
And a meaning to die
But the question to ask is
Why?

Naeem Arhin Balogun (12)
Harris City Academy Crystal Palace, London

Wonders Of Life

You listen to my poem
In your chairs man-made
Which came from a tree
Shaped with a blade.
We are not alone in the world we have made
My wonders of life will never fade.

We think and we learn, we evolve and change
I live in a world, a world of age.
This is the time, the age of technology
But I believe it's a world of philosophy.

People and theories: it's a world of wonder!
Evolution and revolution clash like thunder.
Life is created by the smallest star
the world is still a wonder, a wonder by far.

I am twelve years old and experiences still await
I've had this wonder ever since I was eight
I want to travel and see the world from high
When I'm older I wish to fly.

I wonder where we'll be when we're older
Not so young, but bigger and bolder
I hope this poem has bought you delight
As these are my wonders, my wonders of life!

Selina Belay (12)
Harris City Academy Crystal Palace, London

I Am Fire

I am fire
My soul is yelling with pure frustration
I want to punch someone
Preferably in the face

I am mad
I will destroy the next person that annoys me
I will show no mercy

I am bloodthirsty
My mind screams with crippling anger
I feel like ripping apart walls

I am exploding with negativity
I am clenching my fists
I am ready to fight

I am burning down buildings
The sheer force of my emotion
Is threatening to set loose a terrible monster

I am burning
I am functioning on only the sheer force of my temper

I am a threat
And the world should be scared.

Amy Evans (13)
Harris City Academy Crystal Palace, London

The Dark Tunnel Of My Heart

Every day is dark and lonely.
I don't like this prickly feeling.
I see them criticise me;
My looks, my hair, me only.

I feel their eyes staring at me.
No one ever cares about me.
When they laugh emotions fill me.
Why does it have to be me?

Then one day when I was walking,
Someone came and started talking.
Their light blocked the darkness.
I was in a dark, dark tunnel,
But at the end I saw the light.

Now that I see the light,
I don't feel those eyes criticising me.
Now I feel loved.
Now I can laugh.
And the darkness is all gone.

Chineze Offokansi (13)
Harris City Academy Crystal Palace, London

Imagine Me

Imagine me
Being free
Trusting everyone I see
It's been a while
Since
I've been me

Every day I feel the same
There's just nothing to blame
That keeps me the same
I believe
I could make a change

Happiness is the key
You just need to believe in me

There's a lock
That needs to be free
Just as long as you're with me
I see the light
That controls me.

Imagine me!

Lakeisha Miyanda (13)
Harris City Academy Crystal Palace, London

 # Jealous

J ealousy isn't a good look on you
E verything isn't yours
A ll of your actions don't affect me
L ove is more than a word
O pen mindsets are the way to go
U nderstand, to envy others, is to pity yourself
S immer down.

Trinity Myton (14)
Harris City Academy Crystal Palace, London

Anger

Anger, aggression
They mean the same thing
Caused by the same thing
Jealousy.

A reaction
Like electricity
It flows through your body
Striking at everything.

The anger
It takes over
Everything you do now
It's a reaction.

Don't become us
Educate us
Teach us
Control the reaction
Before it's too late.

Charlie Fletcher (13)
Harris City Academy Crystal Palace, London

Pure And Utter Discontent

D aydreams of how it could be
I n unconditional love with him
S ecret hatred towards her
C ounting the hours till we meet
O n the verge of breaking down
N ot every day smile
T oday I will forget
E nvy will kill your soul
N obody's jealous of you
T oday I will move on.

Bukkiah Param (13)
Harris City Academy Crystal Palace, London

I'm In Love With The Cocoa

I'm in love with the cocoa
Its silky milk taste,
I'm in love with the cocoa
The imperfections of its shape.

I'm in love with the cocoa
My love for it is like real love,
I'm in love with the cocoa
It tastes like it came from Heaven above.

I'm in love with the cocoa
The sensational taste makes me want to faint,
I'm in love with the cocoa
The square cubes it paints.

I'm in love with the cocoa
It's time for me to say goodbye,
I'm in love with the cocoa
I'm going to stick to my apple pie.

Rianna Martin (12)
Harris City Academy Crystal Palace, London

Your Time

Smoke up your tyres to earn your crest
Tune up your engine to be the best
Rev up your motor to slaughter the rest
Everyone ready? Steady?
Too late, go.

Rag your car to the peak
Every drop of mud could cause a leak
Squeeze the accelerator
Pump the clutch
Change the gear
Reach the finish line because it's your time.

Jack Davies
Harris City Academy Crystal Palace, London

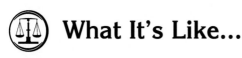

What It's Like...

I have alopecia
Just thought you'd like to know
Right now there's no cure
You just have to learn to cope.

When you first start to notice
It really is a shock
You see a little patch
Then others start to mock.

You get those tedious questions
What happened to your hair?
When you can no longer cover it
Some people start to stare.

A third of them are lucky
Their hair soon reappears
But those that are left behind
Still cry lonely tears.

Jasmine Clarke-Terrelonge (14)
Harris City Academy Crystal Palace, London

Patience

Tick, tock
The sound of the school clock
Patience, patience
I don't know how long I can wait
Can this place really decide my fate?
Will this ever end?
It's getting louder
I see red
I look at the clock
9:48
Now I feel depressed.

Aaliyah Williams (13)
Harris City Academy Crystal Palace, London

Fury

Eyes glazed
Mind hazed
Voices raised
Fists clench
Mood tense
Teeth grit
Attempts to hit
Words spat
No more tact
Tongue hiss
Cheap diss
Blood boils
Hot like oil
Cuts deep
Heart beats
Argument ends
Don't talk to me again.

Khadija Aidoo (14)
Harris City Academy Crystal Palace, London

 # Poetopia

I am large and green, covered in mud
I am home to many worms,
I am very old and worn,
However, my white lines are still bright,
I have been here for many years, nothing changes.

I am a football pitch, as old as a Game Boy,
I want to run away but I can't because
I am a football pitch, as green as a pitch can be,
I lie listening to the whistling wind.

I have to go now, the football teams have arrived,
It is my time to shine, so goodbye for now.

Thomas Rendell (11)
Harris City Academy Crystal Palace, London

 # Broken Wing

Her heart lies empty
You're the only one with her
A tear runs down her rosy cheek
You wipe it off
You look into her deep hurt eyes
Her make-up is running down her angelic face
She didn't need make-up anyway
You stroke her hair
She smiles at you
She knows you will be there for her
She hugs you
Squeezing you tighter with every second that passes
Love is a powerful emotion
But only you can find it . . . you can find her
She leans to you
You put your arm over her shoulder
You mend her broken wing.

Orlin Aleksandrov (14)
Harris City Academy Crystal Palace, London

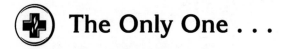 # The Only One . . .

The boy with the song so lovely and long
The one who touched my heart
As I knew he would from the start.

The one with the most annoying name
Who didn't attract me with his fame.

But with his lovely personality
And his awesome nationality

The only one who stands out for me
The only one!

Sadie Duong (12)
Harris City Academy Crystal Palace, London

Just Keep Running

Time takes its toll.
We all grow older.
Letting the days go by
Is all we can do.
Watching the world,
In all of its colours,
They will fade away to grey.
Like the evenings blue.
Not everything is perfect,
In harmony or happy.
You my feel like you are beaten down.
But if you get up,
Just keep on running.
Then maybe
Just maybe
You'll find the truth.

Bryony Pickering (13)
Harris City Academy Crystal Palace, London

How To Tie A Tie

Smile
It looks beautiful on you
Smile
To show how you feel

Laugh
It sounds beautiful coming from you
Laugh
To display how you feel

Cry
It feels beautiful when tears fall on you
Cry
To voice how others make you feel.

Jodi-Rae Dacosta (14)
Harris City Academy Crystal Palace, London

My Little Sister

After walking a mile,
I just wanted to smile,
Seeing my sister's cute, little face,
As she stood waiting in a pretty pink dress of lace,
As I got closer I noticed a trace of a tear down her face.

'Why the long face?' I asked,
She tried to hide it with a laughing mask,
I looked down at her grazed knee,
She carried on looking at me,
She said with a plea, 'Why did you leave me?'

I bent down and kissed her forehead,
'I am sorry,' as I hugged and said,
'Never again will I leave you alone,'
As I handed over an ice cream cone,
Her eyes lit up as she smiled and said, 'You're the best brother ever.'

Talhah Iftakhar (12)
Harris City Academy Crystal Palace, London

What Makes Me

My tears are mute
My hands shake
My lips quiver
Yet I still don't break.

Secrets drown me
Thoughts drive me insane
Gossip bombards me
Yet I don't show my pain.

Anger follows me
Envy crowds me
Sadness haunts me
But that is what makes me!

Fizzah Haq (14)
Harris City Academy Crystal Palace, London

Being A Teenager In Society

Being a teenager in this society
Can sometimes be hard
Being told what to do
Who to be
When all we want to be is us
To be me . . .

Confusion, depression, acceptance
Are all stages of our life
Finding ourselves . . .
Rolling the dice
Knowing who you are
Must be nice . . .

Charlotte Hoez (13)
Harris City Academy Crystal Palace, London

Love And Emotion

I have a smile on my face every time I see you,
You make my heart beat so fast,
Like a race car going through the finish line . . .

I live in a heart race just to see you.
I see you every day but I'm too scared to talk to you,
I'm scared I'll stumble and you'll say, 'I never want to talk to you.'

You make me happy, as if I want to run,
Through a field with butterflies and colourful flowers,
I can't stop smiling when I see you . . .

So this is my poem about you,
So, why don't you come and rhyme with me too!

Courtney Mae Myers (12)
Harris City Academy Crystal Palace, London

School

School is as odd as a penguin being the head
Firstly, the time it takes for you to get out of bed
You walk up the hill and through the snow to find that you had homework, uh-oh
Homework is bad because it makes kids mad
They do it to a low standard which makes the teacher sad
So you get a detention for something you didn't do
And then another for wearing the wrong shoe
So overall, school is as odd as a penguin being the head and giraffes being the pupils.

Anna Richards (11)
Harris City Academy Crystal Palace, London

When I Write

I pick up my pen and I write
Writing is like a maze
I strum my guitar and something's not right
Writing is my escape
When I write colour disappears, everything turns black and white
When I write I feel like Wonder Woman with a cape
If something bad happens it turns out to be alright
That's what it's like being me
The girl obsessed with creativity
I make the most of every opportunity.

Hannah Irons (14)
Harris City Academy Crystal Palace, London

Being A Pre-Teenager

They think they know,
They are utterly wrong,
You're bewildered, lost in your mind,
I wish I could fall like a cascade,
Into suddenly, a dark corner with only
A flicker of light as hope.

When the time comes,
They'll understand,
But right now, we're yearning for a miracle,
Brain buzzing,
Heart pumping,
Is all hope lost?

Soaked in exhaustion,
Bag weighing your shoulders down,
Like someone has purposely fitted one million stones in,
Wish there was hope,
Only neglectfulness, which will soon burst inside me,
Sadness clings, lingers, like a child not letting go.

Soon the ice cracks,
They find out,
They were wrong, totally,
In every possible way,
But now they know,
A new side will grow.

No more loneliness,
Faith is in the air,
Happiness grows, as if it was already there,
Help is at hand,
If ever I feel lost,
Being a pre-teenager is a whole new exciting beginning!

Anise Patel (11)
Lady Margaret School, London

Adventure Of The Day

Puss in Boots, what a cat,
With a hammer, he squishes people flat.

But this is not the cat we know,
This one's awful, such a foe.

Puss was venturing around
When suddenly he heard a loud sound.

This noise sounded a bit like a miaow,
He thought, *well, that can't be a cow.*

Puss turned the corner,
And caught sight of the milk lady, Lorna.

He saw a tail go down another street,
Unwary of the end that it would meet . . .

Puss started to pick up the speed,
This was the perfect level he would need.

Puss finally caught up to the . . . *cat!*
OMG! it looked like a rat!

Puss finally caught up to it,
Getting ready to dig a pit.

He was as ugly as a zit,
But more like Puss than he'd care to admit.

Puss started to dig,
And at the end of it was as dirty as a pig.

That was his adventure of the day,
And he's very proud of it, I must say!

Eva Delaney (11)
Lady Margaret School, London

Love

Love is a wonderful thing
Not just a summer fling
Your heart beats louder than ever
And you cry almost never
Love is looking into the night sky and seeing only light
From the stars burning so bright
Love is as beautiful as a petal
And makes your soul settle
Love is looking at their eyes and seeing into their heart
You are never apart
Love should be cherished
So it will never perish
Love is better than romantic verses
Your heart will never need nurses
To put back together the broken pieces
Because unhappiness ceases
Your eyes bear a twinkle
And it doesn't matter if your face should wrinkle
Because he only sees beauty
And the whole world is wonderful and fruity
You shine every day
And when you walk it is like ballet
My sweet little flower
I give you the power
To rule over my heart
Till death do us part
Then again maybe I'm not the best person to explain
Then again there is usually pain.

Felicity Parker Thomas (11)
Lady Margaret School, London

A Letter To The Adults

They take their notes but they don't understand
How we really are feeling
If they take away our phones and games
We would just lie down and stare at the ceiling.

In groups we're all just menaces
But alone we walk with heads down
We pull our hoods up over our faces
To mask unfriendly frowns.

You think that we're all criminals
Guilty until proven not
But you're not allowed to change your minds
You're cold and then you're hot.

We're children for the most part
And adults when it suits you best
With duties and responsibilities
That limit play and rest.

We are ignorant and foolish
If we don't agree with your way
But you deemed us as rebels
We just want to have a say.

Because we have thoughts and opinions
Hopes for the future too
Please know we're not the enemy
Sincerely, Younger Forms of You.

Sarah-Jayne Lartey (12)
Lady Margaret School, London

Light

Life is a journey,
A very long one,
And there are definitely bumpy roads to come.

But there are straight ones too,
That you will fly through.

You'll be happy sometimes, the moment does come,
You'll do so many things, most will be fun.

Don't spend time worrying, there'll always be light,
And you'll ride off on a horse with a very brave knight.

If you ever feel fear,
Remember, I'll always be here.

To help you through those bumpy roads,
Now this is something no one knows.

Listen carefully,
This is my secret to tell.

There will always be light wherever you go,
Unfortunately, it's time for me to go.

Life is a journey,
A very long one,
And now my ending has come.

But don't worry little girl, your time has just begun,
Now go on, ride off into the sun.

Rebecca Dawit (11)
Lady Margaret School, London

Laughter

Before it was crinkled and shrivelled,
Like a plastic bag in a subsequent storm.
Yearning for happiness,
As if it would never come.

Then within the depths of sadness,
A flicker came alive.
After it had pondered for so long,
Never ever again would it hide.

A lamp in the darkness,
Uplifting everyone.
Negativity is no more,
Away, completely gone.

The face is now full of youth,
Wrinkles are no more.
Positivity stays put,
Jubilant, jolly, jovial.

Laughter, loud and loving,
Giggles so good and great.
A dream of merriness pursued,
Once known, remembered for evermore.

Grace Wilkinson (11)
Lady Margaret School, London

Unexplainable

Half-starved women and men look out towards me,
They stand behind wired fences.
Death every way they turn,
Dark, sunken eyes, looking into the distance,
The pain is unimaginable,
Working all day and night,
Sleeping in groups of six,
A murder of crows look smugly at them,
Laughing and separating the weak from the strong,
Young children who were once laughing and joyful,
Now taken from their parents and never seen again.

He is a murderer of the Jews,
Mad, crazy, destructive,
A dent in history,
How could this happen?
Were people hypnotised into this wicked massacre?
The barbaric murderous man,
Who killed himself in cowardice,
This must not be forgotten, for evermore.

Isabella Osborne (12)
Lady Margaret School, London

Apple Juice

It starts as a seed,
Grows up into a tree.
Red and green balls of delight
You see it glint in the sun,
Oh! How it will result in such fun.
Kevin falls off the tree,
Is picked up, now you see.
Kevin is off to be crushed.

Into bottles, he will be poured.
With labels stuck on the front:
Pure and delicious,
Ripe and ready.

He'll be turned into an advert,
With raining, golden droplets
Seen on every TV screen.

It tastes of heaven
This is . . .
Apple juice!

Sasha Howells (11)
Lady Margaret School, London

Think Positive

Life.
Life is a busy street,
but it can sometimes also be sweet,
It brings you happiness and finds who you really are,
And then you find that you're a bright shining star.

Snow.
Snow is happiness, laughter is in the air,
Taking it away is not fair,
Snow brings out happy children,
It really is very fun!

Sun.
The sun is beautiful; big and bright too!
Sun equals happiness, woohoo!
The sun is a ball of happiness,
Now we don't need to see anymore sadness!

All through tears, happiness will guide you through,
We should make up a club: The Happiness Crew.

Khoula Saeed (12)
Lady Margaret School, London

In A Thousand Years

Aliens come to Earth
And land right on the turf
Kangaroos surf
Men give birth
People wear pants over their heads
And suddenly sharks live in sheds
The new transport what is it
Planes
Trains have no tracks
New fashion, sacks
Worn on your backs
Dogs marry people
And churches have no steeples
Pigs finally learn to fly
And that's the reason
Why.

Sameera Elnaim (11)
Lady Margaret School, London

Trapped

I peer into musty classrooms,
creased workbooks jumbled in piles,
cared for, yet not loved.
Pencils scattered, lights dimmed.

It's strange to think I was once contained in one
of these bleak classrooms,
that once, with a pining glance out of a window,
I lined up to be stuffed with maths
and literature forced in, till my mind split with effort.

Something catches my eye:
a doodle on a corner page.
Desperate curls interweave with figures,
a feeble attempt to escape the flatly ebbing lesson.

We're caught in a circle of repetition:
painful study to good results,
good results to well-paid jobs;
the trap built by our own hands.

A spark of anger flickers through me.
It has been denied them:
the creative arts, the thing they hustle away,
only sometimes to be dragged out,
a drop of fresh water shed on a barren desert.
Don't they understand
that each instinct craves to burst forth
where imagination's creeping vines can explore?

I catch the wrist of a girl running past.
Bright, quick eyes, a darting step.
Is she not happy?
I find a thread of doubt in my beliefs.
'Are you enjoying school?' I ask.

She shrugs. 'I passed all my tests well, if that's what you mean.'

The rhythm of society makes its mark,
Not just to rid ignorance, but also innocence.

Phoebe Mackie (13)
Laidlaw Education Classroom, London

 # Anti-Bullying

My heart thudded as they ganged in,
They chucked my bag in the stinky bin.
They called me names and pulled my scarf,
When my tears fell they had a laugh.

They hit me till I gave them money,
Through my watery eyes it was no longer sunny.
They mocked me till I fell to the ground,
I wanted to scream but I made no sound.

In class they sat next to me,
But only to kick me on the knee.
They treated me kindly in front of the teacher,
When he turned around I was to them a horrid creature.

My journey home was full of gloom,
All I wanted to do was cry in my room.
Those words they said hurt my feelings,
I cried in sorrow like the leaky ceilings.

The next day I did not go to school,
They will just be even more cruel.
I skipped breakfast, lunch and dinner,
By the end of the day I became wary and thinner.

I had no choice but to go to school next morning,
I knew it was a bad day because it was pouring.
As I reached the gates,
I expected to see them and their mates.

But no one and nothing was there but a sign,
It made my face light up and shine.
With the words big and bold,
'*Anti-bullying week*' it told.

I started crying with happy tears,
Someone had understood my fears.
My life had changed from that point,
Our friendship circle is finally joint.

Maimoona Alie (11)
Madani Girls School, London

Dear Dad

I heard the story of the day I was born,
The special moment to you just before dawn,
You gazed at me with those star-like eyes,
Those very eyes that stopped my moans and cries.

You were the perfect parent, my flawless father,
Because you never let us go, you clasped us together.
I was never able to find a fault within you.
To me you were the valiant of lions, the brightest star;
You were with me, no matter how far you really are.

I remember the times when so grievous was Mother,
But you always cheered her up, my doting father.
Motivating you were when we faced challenges,
And when we fell you mended the damages.

However, a time came you were most struggled,
Hoping and hoping for your strength to be doubled.
In severe pain you laid on the hospital bed,
Day and night, for your recovery, we pled.
During those times did Mother feel so desperate,
Wanting to stay with you, she could not be separate.
So mad I was, the doctors could do nothing,
And so to home, they said you were coming.

Then one day, something dire happened.
Everything was so sudden, I hoped it was imagined.
Holding you was Mum and on the phone for your aid was sister,
I was outside hearing your heavy breaths, one after the other,
On the other hand, was my Jaad wailing,
Calming him down, so hard I was trying!

After a while, everything was hushed,
And to your room, I rushed.
There you laid on the ground so still,
I didn't believe it, it wasn't my will.
I joined my family and sat in front of your feet,
And so my insides began to pleat.
Then I asked Mum, 'What did the doctors say?'
Mum said, 'He'll be alright,' but everything seemed grey.
After that I saw sister pump your chest and your feet I touched,
the truth, I finally clutched . . .

No matter how much I was told to be strong,
I couldn't, it felt like a nightmare, everything seemed wrong.
No matter how many times people asked me if I'm okay,
My answer is no, but yes I have to say.
No matter how hard I try to stop my tears to flow,
I can't stop it; it was too sudden for you to go.

Now I can't hug you nor kiss you, nor wait for you after school,
But life has an end, and that's a rule.
I know at least you're in a special place,
I know one day, I'll see your radiant face.
So all I want is for you to be alright,
And I'll come back in your arms the day we reunite.

I love you Dad,
But now it's time for your slumber from the life you had.

Mashrufa Karima
Madani Girls School, London

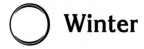 Winter

Winter, winter,
Can't even hear a splinter,
Long and dark are the days ahead,
All I have time for is just a quick bread,
Outside is snow . . . 'Oh glory!' I say,
Now I know it's gonna be a good day.

Everything is white,
Today's a delight,
Forgot to stand upright,
Gushhhh! The wind went,
And there I flew over mini tents.

Oh winter!
That is how powerful it is . . .

Winter, winter . . .

Nazeefa Hussain (11)
Madani Girls School, London

When I'm Gone

When I'm gone,
They'll see what I was worth,
They'll be alone,
and I'll be a lost soul wandering this Earth.
No burden on me, looking at the horizon,
I finally set myself free.

I'm unknown and I prefer being unknown,
To avoid the insinuation, I walk on head held high.
I have no pride, more like pride doesn't want me.
Outcasted for being me. Outcasted for being divergent.

When I'm gone,
They'll see what I was worth,
They'll be alone,
and I'll be a lost soul wandering this Earth,
No burden on me, looking at the horizon,
I finally set myself free.

Everyone expects me to be someone I'm not!
I'm seeking for my role model, yet I am
a role model. I don't even know what I want to be?
Society, family, friends corrupt every belief I
have. Belittle me till I am no more.

They expect too much from us teenagers.
Since day one it's been competition.
Me against you, you against her, her against me.
We are meant to be righteous humans but day by day we become
Iniquitous varmint.

When I'm gone,
that's if I'm gone,
because I'm not ready to leave home.

Every day I walk down the streets,
My streets,
The streets that I grew up in
It's evident that I changed, that I can make decisions for myself
Yet a penetrating feeling leaves me feeling vulnerable
I don't want to grow up . . .

When I'm gone and that's if I'm gone
Because I'm not ready to leave home.

Shazia Alam (13)
Madani Girls School, London

 # The Rage Within Me

Bang my fists on the floor,
Can't take it anymore,
Gotta punch, kick, let it out,
Gotta hold on,
Gotta keep calm,
Gotta show the world that I'm good,
But then the memories come back,
And anger approaches to me once again

So,
I gotta shout out loud,
Gotta slam it down
Screaming, shouting, punching, kicking
Everything going through my head too fast.

But right now,
I can't think straight,
Destroying everything,
That is in my way.

Otherwise,
It's gonna hold me back,
I'll never face it off,
I'll never push it down.

Sadiya Begum (13)
Madani Girls School, London

As I Walked Into This World . . .

As I walked into this world,
I saw nothing but me,
Only a place which could be opened,
By a deadly key.

This nightmare was filled with fear and dread,
Such to be seen by the cursed and the dead,
There was no spark; there was no light,
Only, of which, that could fright.

As I walked into this world,
I saw nothing but me,
Creatures large as buildings,
All waiting behind a lifeless tree.

From the depths of the worst,
Came the monsters and beasts,
Their mouths yearning,
Just for a good meal to eat.

As I walked into this world,
I saw nothing but me,
Only cries of despair,
Wanting to flee.

Menacing hisses and furious growls,
What else was there to come?
All I could do was stand there,
My body all numb.

As I walked into this world,
I saw nothing but me,
Only a place which could be opened,
Wondering aloud I said,
'So this is the world inside me . . . '

Tahiya Ahmed (13)
Madani Girls School, London

◯ Insomnia

Trying to sleep but my eyes wide open,
Voices whispering from every side,
Battles in my mind,
Nowhere to hide,
A futile resistance against the rising tide,
Thought after thought as this constant barrage takes its toll,
Eating away slowly now a gaping hole,
My mind going crazy and out of control.

I search frantically and fail in despair,
For something elusive which was something which was always there,
Something tossed away with out a care,
In a prolonged absence I can no longer bear,
Tossing and turning all night long,
Miserable and sad, everything wrong,
What is life and where do I belong?

Millions of questions,
And answers all long,
My heart is riddled with grief and sorrow,
And with these thoughts my tears flow,
My world is hypocrisy and lies,
And no more good do I recognise,
Everything I possess,
And this voice inside I hear its cries.

So this mission of truth I have when aboard,
With conviction my shield and truth my sword,
Content and happy - no more tears to weep,
Content and happy - I fall asleep.

Shania Musah
Madani Girls School, London

Internal Battle

My thoughts are the same,
Day in and day out,
I've only got myself to blame,
For my lack of self-confidence.

Walking to school,
I see a pretty girl pass by,
Tall. Skinny. Beautiful.
She's society's idea of perfect,
I wonder . . . Why can't I look like her?

Sitting in class,
I gaze at the girl who always has the answer,
Smart. Intellectual. Outgoing.
She's the girl that has predicted 'A' grades
And I wonder . . . Why can't I be like her?

But then, there's always a little part inside,
My conscience, telling me, trying to make me believe,
That I am beautiful and smart in a unique way,
That there is nothing more I need to be happy.

It tells me that I am perfect just the way I am,
And that I should have optimistic thoughts,
Because I won't get far in life,
If I keep looking at the negative factors.

I then cheer up,
It's because I love myself,
I love my flaws and my imperfections,
Because that is what makes me, 'me'.

Sadia Kuddus (13)
Madani Girls School, London

My Anger

Anger is deep within me
Anger is a feeling
Some people take their anger out
On other people, or other things
I tend to do it differently.

Anger drives me crazy
Anger is what turns me on
Anger wants to kill me
Anger is what makes me mad.

Anger is unreasonable
Anger is invincible
Anger is uncontrollable
But why, where, who, what
Brought me so much anger?

Some people write when they are angry
Some people draw
Me, I'm not like any of those people at all
I don't let my anger show to anyone but me
I keep my anger within me.

Ilhan Ibrahim (14)
Madani Girls School, London

Friendship Is Gold Dust

Friendship is extremely valuable,
Which I think is highly reasonable,
It makes you feel all warm inside,
Someone who's always by your side,
Friendship's beauty is like sandy bays,
The waves glittering in all different ways.

Friendship is like gold dust.
Good friendships never rust.

Radeyah Chowdhury
Madani Girls School, London

Fallen Angels

We fell down with a thud,
Lying there
On the cold, hard ground
Not worthy to stay there

Our wings were gone,
They were submerged
Into our shoulder blades,
For we were not good enough
To keep our wings,
Standing there
With sadness in our eyes

Deep in our thoughts
We recalled
This burden we carried
Oh! So heavy
It pushed us down.
Now we lie here with nothing
But our burdens,
We no longer belonged.

Fiore Tasnim Razzak (13)
Madani Girls School, London

Hush

'Hush,' she said, 'don't tell anyone I'm here'
Hushed, I was, my throat constricted by fear
'Hush,' she said, 'I'm not going to hurt you'
Hushed, I was, as I wondered who
'Hush,' she said, 'the ash is beginning to fall'
Hushed, I was . . . the ash did start to fall.

And the darkness came, in the form of feathers
Feathers fell; black snow with blades
I heard a call, loud and clear
'Hush,' she said, 'for it is near'
I felt my tears, but not from me
From the clouds above, unable to flee

The glass began to break
And the gravel on the ground shook
My soul had escaped
An oblivion awaits
I know I'm doomed, for evermore
'Hush,' she said, 'Dissimilis has arrived.'

Sadia Choudhury (13)
Madani Girls School, London

Fake Living

Walking around with pain in my chest,
Not a moment of rest.
My life is full of stress,
Can't do this no more: fake living.

Smiling to passers-by,
Inside it's all a lie.
Trying to hold my breath, but once again let out a sigh,
Can't do this no more: fake living.

Running around in circles,
Popping myself open from trapped bubbles,
The speech I prepared doesn't come out in verbal,
Can't do this no more: fake living.

Living in a place where I am a mistake,
The pain is bigger than a lake.
Feeling of me being alone aches,
Can't do this no more: fake living.

Labiba Tahsin (13)
Madani Girls School, London

 # Dear Past

Your attempts to have me destroyed
Devastates my soul considerably.
You are one entity to avoid
For you cause distress and misery.

Haunting me through sleepless nights
Tackling me on my worst of days
I've learnt to confront these emotional frights
To lead my life in challenging ways.

Giving up isn't an option - I'm determined to thrive.
Holding onto this thread of hope, ever so tight
The hunger within me pushes me to strive
In order for my future to be somewhat bright.

You are my weakness doing me wrong
Thinking about you brings me unease
So I must suppress the past to remain strong
The agony endured, desperate to release.

I want to escape and be set free . . .

Yours Present.

Zainab Sheikh Rabiah (14)
Nightingale Academy, London

Dear Me

This is an apology letter.
I'm sorry for shoving unnecessary things in you
and not making room for the good things.

I'm sorry for mistaking you for clay. You were (are)
not meant to be moulded to suit anyone's needs.

I'm sorry for not realising you are already wonderfully
built just the way you are.

I'm sorry for scarring you with my own claws of destruction
and hate.

I'm sorry for making a home in dark places and for
continuing to do so.

I'm sorry for placing sticky notes on your failures
and regrets rather than marking down your triumphs and dreams.

I'm sorry for not being there for you when you
needed me because I was too busy drowning in
annihilating thoughts.

I'm sorry for not appreciating and seeing you for who you are
because I got blinded by who you are supposed to be,
how you are supposed to act
and what you are supposed to do.
I foolishly let myself get shackled by society and its expectations.

I'm sorry for slapping you on the face with callous
words and for making you accept and believe
those words.

I shouldn't have made you feel worse about yourself
than you already do.

I'm sorry for continuing to search for
train wrecks, broken roads, mishaps and deserts in you.

I'm sorry for hurting you physically, mentally
and emotionally so often that you're becoming
numb to the pain.

I'm sorry for not loving you completely and whole-heartedly.

Luiza Janavciute (14)
Nightingale Academy, London

She's Slowly Dying

She's slowly dying,
Lying out on the ground.
Her wrists are slashed,
Dripping blood,
On the floor, it's all around.

She could take the pain no longer,
Inside it had begun to get stronger.
Her heart releases the grief,
Releases the doom.
Her head turns as she looks at the moon,
She whispers, 'It will be over soon.'
But inside she's not ready to die,
And with that thought she begins to cry.

But she just won't carry on,
Her life is fading,
Her fight is waning.
She carried on like a soldier with a battle wound
Bleeding out from every cut she consumed.

It's all over,
All gone, she took her final breath.
Now she's greeting Death.

She lies there,
Her blood no longer flowing,
Her pain no longer showing.

Can you see what the world has done to her fight?
With every word the light began to dim.
She committed the act,
But this is a fact,
The world should bow down its head in shame.

Alice Louise Baxter (15)
Nightingale Academy, London

The History Of The Land Of Marion

Remember our Land of Marion
The natural, tropical lakes and flawless waterfalls
And the whistling of the birds that recalls
The anthem of Marion.
Don't you remember?
The rainfall that spat on our roofs with a swift trickle
The exploding volcanoes in the distance with a tickle
Whilst we played Chinese whispers as a pastime.
You can't have forgotten?
How about the luxurious houses we all used to dwell in
And our children that would play together and have so much fun in
Please . . .

It was Him wasn't it?
He made you forget our times of connectivity
The times of peace and prosperity
All scrapped because of His failed attempt to communicate interactively.
Yet we did nothing to trigger this,
He captures us separately
And isolates us in his white box.
Like an island; distanced away from the world
That was why . . . right?
To remind us of his past and how he was manipulated brutally
He erased our memory, keeping one brain lesion alive
To leave as a memory to be deserted by
And never find a way out
Just like he couldn't.

Remember what Grandmother used to say
About the change in democracy, she used to say
And how each feature that gave a spark in Marion
Only to now be left all alone.
Remember what Father used to say
About our free time and how it should be used,
Although his leisure time was hypocritically wasted
through vodka and whisky
Alcohol, beer and anymore of that disgusting trash
Effective to the result of his death . . .

So what's our solution?
What do we do?
Is it stay in this prison for all of eternity
Or find the key for the locks?
Which will it be?
Being served the food
Or eating the food.
Maybe so, a brand new car
Or actually driving it.
Let's do what we can
We may seem clueless
But only if we accept ourselves
Being portrayed this way.
I've thought of a plan
A strategic plan
Are you with me?

Robel Asmelash (13)
Nightingale Academy, London

Society's Eyes

Looking into society's eyes,
Telling yourself nothing is wrong.
You never began to realise,
You've been neglected for so long.

They're never really there,
They never truly try.
And every time you surely need them,
They make up inconceivable lies.

'Why are they like this?'
You wonder and cry.
They see you are broken to pieces,
But they watch you and walk by . . .

Trapped, torn, tormented,
You tell yourself to be strong.
You feel like you're used to it,
This is what it was always like; lifelong.

Your dreams are to glisten,
Shine like a diamond ring.
'You'll slowly reach there,' you tell yourself,
But you've injured a wing.

They say all that matters is your wellbeing,
Although they've mistreated you for so long.
You cannot believe the hardships you're witnessing,
But there are consequences to life, you have to persevere and play along.

Your problems start to interfere with your personality,
Some of them which you can't share.
Every valuable thing has ups and downs,
And the pleasant aftermath will hold your hand, as long as you care.

They hate you for being different,
Individuality means being unacceptable.
Hatred?
We have plentiful . . .

You have exceeded complications,
Society does not care.
You're holding on to the fine line between life and death,
Life just isn't fair.

That's what it is like to grow up here,
Sometimes you don't stand a chance.
You always live by a fear,
Only daring to look at the world with a single glance . . .

Meryemcan Meydan (14)
Nightingale Academy, London

 # Danger Zone!

The adrenaline that makes you stronger,
The death that brings glory,
The determination that makes you survive,
The pain and misery that never ends,
The hunger that eats all your might . . .

The faces that will be replaced,
The names that puzzle your head,
The lives that will be gone,
The future that will be killed,
The arrows in their body,
The ceaseless, low cry fading away . . .

The killings that make you win,
The true passion that will make everything seem easy,
The luck that will be there forever,
The knife that will be thrown in their body,
The tears that will be wiped away,
The training that will be paid off . . .

The hunting that reveals the patience of death,
The blue, tranquil sky eventually turning to grey,
The danger everybody feels,
The struggles that will be forgotten,
The thick, red liquid rolling down from their heads,
The colour red that resembles 'pain'.

Hayat Aden (14)
Nightingale Academy, London

Handling Things

Handling things isn't easy.
Juggling this, juggling that
Maybe I'll even fit in time to see my dad.

Oh wait, yeah I forgot
He left a long time ago.
Not a goodbye
Never another hello.
I hang on
To every hello ever said
And remember, it means way more
Than a goodbye.

All up in my head
Thinking.
If you were here,
Would it be better
Or worse?

All up in my feelings.
Fighting against
If I love you
Or not.

You were an important piece of my life.
Not just the fact that
You contributed to giving me life.
Just for the simple fact of,
You taught me to not need anyone
'Cause no one ever really needs you.

So here you go.
This one's for you, Dad.
Or should I say, Wayne.

Ashli Rodney (13)
Nightingale Academy, London

A Little Flower's Diary

I slowly arise from my slumber,
The Earth giving to me what I need.
I blossom of purples and blues,
My growth requires great heed.

For the sunshine is my mother,
So the soil is my father.
But the air may be cold,
So what? I am bold.

Shooting up,
I am free from the ground.
For I have made it!
My beauty is bestowed around.

Snip, snip, I am free!
My life flashes before my eyes.
For I am just a humble bluebell and that's all.

Jada Hurgus (14)
Nightingale Academy, London

 # A Teenager

My life is a never-ending
Pit of darkness.
I'm falling, falling,
Into a mass of emotions.
Fear and anger swarm me,
I'm alone with no hope.
Suffering inside,
But nobody knows.
A teenager,
Sad and broken.

Chloe Braganca Vasconcelos
Notting Hill & Ealing High School Senior Department, London

My Teenage Life

Have you ever just thought what it is like to be a teenage girl in this day and age?
I mean, I know, that once upon a time everyone was a teenager
But were they a teen, like me?
No.
Now let me tell you a little tale,
I was bullied. But this is no sob story,
No need to be sorry.
I have many insecurities,
Like, for example, my weight, my looks and my height.
Girls that I thought were my friends,
Only stabbed me in the back to start a fight.
I should have used all of my intelligence and might,
Because then, I wouldn't have been crying,
That very night . . .
I smile and I joke all around,
My laugh only covers my pained frown,
People perceive me as indestructible,
It's bravado.
I'm broken down like shattered glass and rubble.
Do not tell me, 'I know how you feel'
When my feelings aren't really a big deal.
You tell me you are my friend,
And will always be here until the end.
But in reality you are only there
At my glory, not my despair.
Why do I battle with two of me?
Why am I in this great big mess?
Is social media all they see?
Because that life gives me a lot of stress.
You shout and you scream to make me upset,
I can't handle this, I'm getting depressed.
I feel so lonely, I feel so sad.
They say bad times don't last forever,
So if they don't,
Please pull me to the light,
So I can finally be glad.

Tara Alam (13)
Palmers Green High School, London

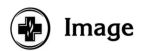 # Image

It's all around her,
Reminding her every day,
Almost in every magazine, tabloid or picture.
Why won't it just go away?

Every image lowers her self-esteem,
Makes her want to hide away,
Concealing herself from the rest of the world
Crying night and day.

Is she happy with the way she looks?
Is she happy with who she is?
Or does she want to be like them
Caked in make-up and afraid to show her real identity.

Sometimes she wonders why,
Why she can't be like them,
Why she is who she is,
Why she wasn't born like them.

But then she realises
She can be anyone she wants to be
She doesn't have to be afraid anymore
And can be the true person everyone really knows her to be.

Elizabeth Andrews (13)
Palmers Green High School, London

Words Are Not Enough . . .

You were always there to make me laugh,
You were always loyal to me,
I made so many mistakes in life
But you were always there to make my life complete and perfect

You stood out from everyone else,
Like a star shining bright.
You've helped me through hard times
You've seen me die inside my soul.

For all the times you've been there
You have always made me happy
You have always made me smile
Even if I cry.

You call to say hello
You call to say you love me
When we are together
A special memory is made.

Well, what can I say?
Without you I feel incomplete
When I close my eyes I think of only you
We have had the best times when we are together.

Thanks for knowing how I feel
Thanks for caring
Thanks for accepting me for who I am
Thanks for always being there for me.

When you cry, I cry
When you smile, I smile
My happiness is in you
There's not one second I haven't thought about you.

We take so many pictures together
But I don't need them
Because I have a mind full of memories
And a heart full of happiness -
When you left me I felt like a shattered piece of glass
But I just wanted to say I love you.

I always will and have loved you even if you're miles away from me.
Words are not enough to explain how much I love you
Even if you don't care about me, I love you still.

Shrishti Mishra (14)
Palmers Green High School, London

 # Promises

You promise me:
'Don't worry! Everything is good!
There is no economic crisis'
You are in a cheerful mood.

You say the people are not homeless . . .
But I have been outside -
So tell me, are you going to help,
Or are you going to hide?

Will you end corruption?
You promise it doesn't exist.
Or free the innocent criminals
On your ominous list?

No. There will be no change I know,
For you are rich and powerful.
Every night to your mansion you go,
And wonder how to trick us next.

I do not want to be in your position,
For being a politician is really not my thing,
But you should stop jailing the opposition
And let their voices sing.

Sophie Etinger (13)
Palmers Green High School, London

My Generation

When I was young,
I didn't care what people thought,
My mum bought my clothes for me,
I was who I was.

I'm not saying I wouldn't love to have a perfect body, hair and personality,
Our society cares too much about what people think of them,
It's in our humanity.

My generation have a fear of what other people say,
And how popular they are,
They don't think about working hard,
So that one day they could pay for a house and a car.

Their priority is to take a nice selfie to post online,
To get 'this' many comments, or 'that' many likes,
When at the end it just causes jealousy,
And you find yourself arguing in a fight.

Teenagers are constantly selling their life story online,
But are they actually enjoying what they're doing?
Or are they too busy trying to take a photo,
To make it seem like they're having a good time?

Maybe elderly people have a point when they say,
'We didn't have that when we were young,'
Because look at them they're full of memories and experiences,
They actually went out and had fun.

The amount of problems caused by social media is incredible,
It's just caused jealousy and insecurity,
Why can't we be happy with what we've got?
We all have purity.

We are trapped, trapped within other people's comments and thoughts,
When I'm old I want to remember actual memories, happy ones,
Not how many likes I got on that photo,
Just look back on social media for a second, what has it actually brought?

I know after this poem you are going to go back and forget,
But I want to live my life how I want it to be,
Not how you, he, she or they want me to,
And yes, I go on social media, but I will always be me.

Ellé-Mae Taylor (14)
Palmers Green High School, London

 # True Friendship

Friendship is based on love and respect,
To be there together, whatever comes next.
To look out for each other in dark times and good,
Because believe me, in life, not everyone would.

Friendships run deep, as deep as the sea,
It comes at no cost, it's just you and me.
To know you are there at the end of the phone
And to feel all the time that you aren't alone.

Friendship is something that, with luck, can last forever,
Will I forget my best friend? I hope not, never.
From the first early years through school and play,
'Best friends forever' you all hear us say.

School days end, university begins,
New friends to meet and learning new things.
A new way of life, promising and true.
But good friends remain constant; they help you get through.

In good times and bad, friendships can be
the best thing in life, I'm sure you'll agree.
Everybody needs to have love on their side.
Someone to be there at times when you've cried.

I'm loyal and true and will be on your side.
I'm always beside you, I'm not going to hide.
We are in this together whatever life brings -
Just being together will help give us wings.

Georgia Catherine Harris (13)
Palmers Green High School, London

What Do You See When You Look At Me?

What do you see when you look at me?

Do you see my dark brown eyes?
My white-toothed smile?
Or my face completely covered
By my pretty hairstyle?

My rosy pink cheeks?
Or when my eyes take a peek?
Because without all my make-up,
I think that I look weak.

I don't see how you can love me
I feel like just a fraud.
I don't get why you say I'm perfect,
When I am so hideously flawed.

There are others who look better,
Effortlessly cool.
But when I try to be myself,
I simply feel like a fool.

I need to stop pretending.
Need to show them who I am.
I don't think I can do it,
But you tell me that I can.

I need to know you're there for me.
There to dull the pain.
Help me through the darkest times,
Keep me normal and sane.

What do you see when you look at me?

Do you see oddly-shaped eyes?
My secretly sad smile?
Do you see a small girl,
Who's been hurt for a long while?

This is who I am,
Who I'm meant to be.
What you really see
When you truly look at me.

Sophiya Syed (14)
Palmers Green High School, London

 # So, Who Am I Going To Be?

One day I'll have to decide who I am going to be -
A normal person, or a person who's going to rule like queen bee
I could be cool, like the new Ice Cube who meets the new Ice-T
Or meets two live crew or be the new Spike Lee
Or be a superhero like Bruce like Wayne, or Bruce like Lee
It's my decision, so who am I going to be?

Now lately it's been hard to tell my friends apart from my enemies
Because plenty of people show me love but in their hearts they envy me
But what hurts the most was being so close and having so much to say
But then finding out that I had to walk away.
I can dwell on the past hurt and swell -
It's my decision, so who am I going to be?

History repeats itself that's just how it goes
You can be somebody so special or just let it flow -
Elvis did it with rock and roll
Then came Justin Timberlake, Eminem and then Macklemore
Long live my idols, may they never be my rivals
It's my decision, so who am I going to be?

Can I live without pretending?
Love without depending?
Listen without defending?
Speak without offending?
Can I think about the future, but still be reminiscing?
So who am I going to be?

Nicole Carrera (13)
Palmers Green High School, London

Time To Shine

I'm on the stage, where I really belong,
The only place I've ever felt at home.
As I belt out the notes and the crowd applaud,
Escaping my life which truly is flawed.

I dream of a life of fortune and fame,
Anything to get me away from this pain.
People tell me, 'Get your head out the clouds,
You're not cut out for this industry,' their words are too loud.

Years of bullying simply because I'm different,
Not your idea of pretty, the insults consistent.
I tell myself, 'It's all just jealousy.'
But everything's just hell to me.

Now's the time to prove them all wrong,
I've wanted this for far too long.
The time is now, the curtains rise,
My life depending on this night.

I'm on the stage, where I really belong,
The only place I've ever felt at home.
As I belt out the notes and the crowd applaud,
No need to escape, life is no longer flawed.

Sophia Panayi (13)
Palmers Green High School, London

 # St Valentine

St Valentine, St Valentine
Bring me love with chocolates
And roses and gorgeous white doves

St Valentine, St Valentine
He was mine
We should have been together till the end of time

St Valentine, St Valentine
From up above
Pray for him gracefully
He's still my one true love

St Valentine, St Valentine
Give us one more chance
Send him down from Heaven
So we can have our final dance.

Portia Stoddart (13)
Palmers Green High School, London

 # Dissimilis

Without Dissimilis, there cannot be life.
Dissimilis is the cataclysm of Man, but
They will make you believe
that it is a gift,
Because the truth is
Dissimilis is the nadir of our race.
It is wrong to think that
we are unique and matchless and exceptional, and should live accordingly.
Instead,
we must abide by the factions, and act as others do.
It is wrong to think that
Dissimilis is something to desire.
In fact,
it is something to fear.
They say
like a dirt road by a highway
Dissimilis is an adventure,
but I don't want this.
Our factions give us
The comfort and security we crave as humans -
Why fight back?
Live by the rules
Don't
Disobey
Dissimilis
(Read now from bottom to top).

Amed Yones (15)
Plumstead Manor School, London

Good Luck For Tomorrow

And do you know what I hate?
I hate how people do not appreciate,
I hate how humans don't love,
And live as if some are below or above
We will die sooner or later as equals
Why can't we be at peace?

There are billions of people in this world,
Yet not one knows the value of one.
You see figures, while I see people.
People with heart,
People who breathe, live and survive with their families
That was before your greed,
Took theirs apart.

Look at that woman,
Her dry eyes no longer shine.
Wrinkles in her face resemble rings in chopped trees.
That will be her soon, that could be me,
Gone and used.
Despised and unmourned.

Ripped and torn, by a life's thorn,
Our lives are scorned,
When really, it should be adorned,
For we were simply, *born.*

Kajma Thapa (15)
Plumstead Manor School, London

⃝ Another Woman

I felt it earlier,
The secrecy,
Lingering in the tense atmosphere that hung between us.
Lingering,
Waiting,
Ready.

I know why.
Although you deny it, I know.

They called you again.
I know,
Yet
You proceed to hide the truth from me.
I know nothing of what they tell you, except that they are wrong.

I can no longer fight against another.
Another who possesses a force I cannot seize;
Will not possess.
I can no longer fight against another you intently rely on.
No longer fight against another you strive to believe.
No longer fight against another who controls you more than I ever have, can or will.
I can no longer fight,
I will no longer fight
Another.
Another woman.

Another woman who longs for you like I do.
Another woman who toys with you.
Another woman who gets thrills from you.
Another woman who loves you.

For I,
My love,
Have given up
My fight;
Have given up
My battle.

Allow another woman to manipulate you into doubting our love and our trust?
I will not
Our love and our trust that we

Spent years building yet
She holds the ability to smash
It down in touches,
Whispers,
Smiles.

Our love
And
Our trust.

I have given up.
Have given up relentlessly pursuing her,
Given up asking if she has called,
Given up waiting for the call,
Given up wanting this to end.
I have given up. And

I will continue to give up
For so long as she shall fight.

Georgia-Rose Beahan (15)
Plumstead Manor School, London

Untitled

It wasn't fair how they used him
After everything he did
It wasn't fair how they experimented on him
All he had to offer, bottled up with a lid.

They changed him
Acted like they made him
When truly all along, he made them
Never once tried to change them.

But what he had was never enough
They kept 'inventing' more and more stuff
He didn't want to give up
So he gave them all he had
It made them go mad.

Potions and remedies, even more
Until he had no more to offer
And then they went to war
With each other, mother and brother.

He was tired by now
Yet they still carried on
'Come on!' they pestered
He burst out, 'How?'

It was over and it was too late
They had ruined their world
The one who was made for their sake
Now how would they ever live or learn?

Ada Ndubuisi (14)
St Anne's Catholic High School For Girls Lower School, London

 # Mindfield

The laughs of the people filled my head
But my cries couldn't shake the foundation my feet didn't try to.
My heart bore my sorrow, my eyes screamed my pain
Yet still it wasn't enough.

I lay in bed
The scenes that I hated replayed in my head
My life was hanging by a split end thread
And all anyone could do was watch
Not that they cared.

I grew up hearing that rhyme about sticks and stones
The phrase killing me slowly as I fought with words as well as actions
So I painted myself with blood and framed the picture with 3D scars
That hurt more than anything.

The world was a battle
But my mind was the field
My fate can't be decided by a faction, so why make it so
I'm more than a title
I'm more than a name
They may not say so but
Life is more than a game.

Abigail Williams (13)
St Anne's Catholic High School For Girls Lower School, London

The Special Day

The day approaches closer and closer
Not sure what might happen
I could feel the love that might flow
To and from the horizon
But still I don't quite know
When it will catch my attention.

Through the darkness of midnight
I am still wide awake
Not convinced someone will choose me
So therefore I shake
Even when I try to sleep
My face looks baked.

As the day is outside my door
I hear people say
'She's my one true love'
Or 'he's my boy'
And someone knocks on my door
Saying, 'Happy Valentine's Day.'

I gleam from surprise and happiness.

Sophia Alighanbari (13)
St Anne's Catholic High School For Girls Lower School, London

A Better You

You build a wall so high that no one can knock it down,
Even then they would only see half of you,
Because you changed yourself, trying to hide your frown,
You hide when they try to help you because you don't want them to,
To isolation and escapism you are bound.

When you try and try but it's only your insides that scream,
They made you like this, it was nothing to do with you,
They made you feel better off in your dreams,
Whilst they were stomping on your heart with their shoe,
But deep down there is something inside you that wants to gleam.

If you fight and fight you will win
Eventually you will succeed.
Those people will probably end up cleaning your bins
When it comes to your life you must lead
Up high is where you should hold your chin.

Higher than your wall
Because you're the only one who can make it fall.

Chloe Jo Hennigan (13)
St Anne's Catholic High School For Girls Lower School, London

✚ Light

Darkness all around me
With nowhere to flee
In this agonising pain
My soul is plain
Screaming in vain

But in all the suffering
I tried to find light
Light lets me fight
Light lets me live
Light is my escape

Dawn never breaks
In this world of melancholy
Joy never comes
To this world of despair
And mercy never shows up
In this world of cruelty

The current was dragging me down
The present taking me on
Giant whirlpools of fear
Drawing me near
There was no light to push me on
No light to show the way

But I see a spark
Then a glimmer
With renewed strength
I swam towards it
Tears down my cheek
Fears floating away

The warmth of the light
Felt just right
Darkness never comes
To this world of light
My heart jumps in joy
As I bobbed in the ocean of wonder.

Atheeth Benny (12)
St Bonaventure's School, London

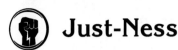 # Just-Ness

Justice, justice
Hard yet yielding
Transparent yet opaque
Old but not ancient.

Fairness is ageless
Needed for generations
Corruption continuing
To snap at its heels.

Law does not sleep
As the sirens always beep
Can we be sure
That justice will be done?

Michael Ogoli (12)
St Bonaventure's School, London

 # A Special World

A special world for you and me
A special bond one cannot see
Its fingers spread like fine spun gold
It holds together, you and me.

Gently nestling us to the fold
Like a thread it holds us fast
Bonds like this are meant to last.

And though at times a thread may break
A new one forms in its place
To bind us closer and keep us strong
In a special world, where you and me belong.

Tomas Augustauskas (11)
St Bonaventure's School, London

Fire Power

I glimmer, like a fading silhouette
I devour my prey like a starving vulture
But with a distorted structure
I make no sound as I scorch and disintegrate my prey, bit by bit
I turn into raging red which can also be spread
Like a cancerous disease
Moving on a swift breeze
I am almost untouchable and yet still visible
Sometimes I can reach out and touch your soul
And make your goal in life
Come true, like the will of fire.

Davesh Rajeev (13)
St Bonaventure's School, London

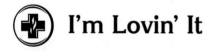

I'm Lovin' It

Are you from McDonald's?
Because I am loving it.

Big Mac, McChicken Sandwich and fries.
I go crazy over hearing all these lies,
Of it being made out of blood,
But all it's made out of is love.

The Coke bottle sweating from the intense heat,
Oh how you wish you could have some of this meat.
The steam hits my face, like a train on a track.
Don't even try and hold me back.

But don't fear, no MSG included.
No such thing as meals and desserts being secluded.
Dip your fries in your McFlurry if you want.
So spread the word from your friends to your aunt.

Come join us for a world of food,
It will all depend on your mood.

Gulden Kurtoglu (14)
The Bridge Academy, London

We Will See...

The darkness has gone, I know, we'll see,
Memories just linger of you and me,
Looking for hope, a place - to be,
If only, if only, we will see . . .

My mind is my faith, my peaceful temple,
Others describe it as evil and mental,
No one has noticed my hopes and dreams,
But I know that one day, we will see . . .

I have a dream, just like Martin,
I have potential, did that leave you laughing?
Alone, alone, as I write my story,
But don't call me selfish when I keep my glory.

A monster you may see in me but I am king,
Who will lead many nations and love from within,
You may call me hopeless,
But one day I'll win,
This is no lie, this is no sin.

My soul was lost in deadly lies,
Empty dreams and curdling cries,
I went to God who was surprised,
He said, 'Find yourself - be wise.'

This isn't just a piece of paper, entered for competition,
This is *my* battle; your astonishment is *my* petition,
The words pour from my heart as this poem is written,
In hope to share how my heart has been bitten.

Death is no option, it leads to more pain,
But life I guess, is just the same.
I could go on with this poem not ending,
Do you now understand, are you comprehending.

No one will know how it is to be me, but there *will* be one day . . .
Where we will see . . . Me.

D'Maire A . D Smith (14)
The Bridge Academy, London

Terrorism Isn't Islam

I see like you,
I hear like you,
I feel like you.

I have family,
I have friends,
I have people I love,
Just like you.

I have dreams,
I have hopes,
I want to grow up and be the one,
That rises above the skies,
And has success, bears no lies.

Yet you view me like I'm a monster,
You say I'll grow up and be the bomber,
You say we're dumb, evil and rude
And bloodthirsty is our only mood.

You say we only want people to pay,
To bleed to death and quietly say,
'We accept your religion and hope you stay,
We won't mick, or take it away.'

You say we kill, with all our will,
Label us as terrorists,
Publish, list and propaganda it
But what about the Nazis?
Or the troops in Afghanistan?
Do they not cause terror?
Then why is it just us?

If some people of our religion,
Goes against, causes confusion,
It doesn't mean you label us all,
Calm your mind and give it a thought.

Britain, a first world country,
Modern, equal and quite understanding,
Yet now the government wants to introduce a bill,
Stop Muslims from having their own free will.

What is this?

What's happening?
It's quite disgusting,
Repeating the actions of the past,
Destroying our future,
What a hoax.

Yes, I'm a Muslim,
Yes, I believe in freedom,
Yes, I'm a human

Just like you.

Masuma Hadi (14)
The Bridge Academy, London

 # The Beauty

The day I met you
I loved you
I didn't have to look at you
The marble reflected your beauty
That's the only thing I had to look at.

Her eye blended in with the blue water
I jumped in, she wasn't there
Her emotion gave power to love
Her eyes shone like a shooting star
She has a future, she has a life
Follow her to make life easier.

My cheeks were like sunset
From the love I gave her
My heart was pumping for the embarrassment.

The love of power
The emotion of love
This gave love
And it ends with love
She said yes, I thought
I was in Heaven, flying.

Azad Ekinci (12)
The Bridge Academy, London

I Lost The Love Of My Life

War came so sudden,
The men had to go to war,
The women had to go and look after the kids,
But we didn't have any yet.

I gave my man a kiss and a pat on the back for good luck
With my bright smile,
He smiled back at me and walked away slowly,
I wanted to stop him but couldn't . . .
He just seemed to be so far away,
No matter how many times, I, reach, I just couldn't
Yet he gave me a smile which seemed so sad.

I sat by the window and waved bye for my man
And waited for his safe return.
I saw them walking away slowly from us,
Then disappeared slowly away,
A tear rolled down my eyes to my cheek,
But I quickly wiped it away,
And told myself, 'I've got to be strong!'

Days, weeks, months passed and yet no sign of him,
I prayed and worried about him at the same time.
A letter finally arrived,
I got the letter and slowly opened it,
I saw what it said . . .
And froze,
I dropped the letter,
Then I dropped onto my knees,
Tears quickly rolled out of my eyes
And down my cheek like a waterfall,
I covered my face with my hand and cried even harder,
I couldn't stop crying,
I realised that I'd lost the love of my life.
The man that I loved so much,
He was so kind yet so scary but he cared for me.
His smile was so warm it cheered me up when I was upset.

I went to my chair beside the window,
Looked outside with my tears still rolling,
I looked out at the window to the sky,
Past the cloud,

I saw my man smiling down at me,
And still his smile is still warm,
And I know for sure he's still in my heart
And memories somewhere, warm and happy.
I smile but tears still come out
For I know he's gone,
But he is still inside me.

Xin Wu (12)
The Bridge Academy, London

 # Life Was Wonderful

Life was wonderful
Life was calm
But now all you have to do is pray for equality
And get guns pointed at you
Life's powerful diversity is slowly being crushed
Under the excessive weight of unfair judgement.
It's hard to believe that we live in a world
Where it's seen as acceptable to kill people just for the way they live.
Our world has been neglected of love and peace
And has now been pillaged by discord and hate.
All this discrimination and war is sure to lead
To the human race's slow and painful demise
Like smoking
However, my anger and opinion will go unheard
and will just fade into a dark void of despair
And will be forgotten like the peace we left behind
And when someone dies they won't be mourned
No one will care enough to shed a single, meaningful tear
All hope and love is lost and can't be restored
The damage has been done and the wound inflicted will never deal
But if it does, it will leave an ugly scar.

Ellie Ryder (13)
The Bridge Academy, London

State Of Shock

Waves of panic,
Water. Not just panic,
Real water, cold and clear,
Filling up this cage.
Cage? I'm in a glass cage,
And I'm going to drown.

My legs are drenched,
More freezing liquid surrounds my waist,
I'm numb, all senses lost,
Nothing but pain and panic is left.
Too cold, too loud, too scared,
Can't move, help me please.

Shivers run up my spine,
Backwards waterfalls:
Waterfalls of worry.
Pain erupts from my ears,
The water like lava,
The pipe it runs from, the volcano.

Pressure builds, the pressure's too much,
And with the water pressure growing,
My pressure to escape rises.
The pressure rises like the bubbles;
The bubbles burst from me,
Like poisonous jellyfish.

My lungs burn,
As if scorched by an absence,
The absence of oxygen,
But not only my lungs are ablaze,
No, the cold flame of terror burns bright too,
Smouldering within me, telling me to get out.

The pain and shock is too much,
All rationality is gone along with air,
Oh, precious oxygen, I long for it,
I beg as the bubbles torrent from my screaming mouth,
I scream, but no one hears me,
I'm alone and dying, here in my vacuum of panic.

This is my state of shock,
This is my state of panic,
My inescapable dream of dread,
This is my death,
This is my end, but then I realise,
I realise the most important of all:
This cold, clear cage is cracked.

Kimberley Crisfield (12)
The Bridge Academy, London

 # Depression

You're drowning.
Sure, the water's shallow,
But you're drowning.
People are above you and their faces are blurry,
But you can see them clear enough.
Loved ones, family, friends.
They seem oblivious,
Oblivious to the fact that you're drowning.
You try swimming up,
But there are weights pulling you down again,
Deeper this time.
How deep can you get pulled?
It's only shallow.
The answer is inevitable,
You get pulled deeper the more you dwell in your pain.
Soon, it'll be a black abyss of nothingness.
You'll feel and be more alone than previously.
And for what?
People like to dwell in their own sadness;
It's called *depression*.

Sophie Langsdon (13)
The Bridge Academy, London

The War Rages On

The war rages on
While the bodies pile upon each other
Nature's tranquillity gone in the blink of an eye
The bombs killing all of the children
The anger through their veins
For the situation of life or death
The lives lost for ours
The fighting causing hell
Blood spilt across the world
Blood on the fighter's hands
And yet the war rages on
Innocent lives gone as fast as the wind could blow
Gunfire piercing through the lives of the fierce fighters
Why is this happening?
Planes hovering above our heads so far the naked eye couldn't see
The sea contaminated with boats armed to the teeth
The men running towards their death and making death with their deadly
weapons
No survivors left
No prisoners taken
No mercy
Why is this happening?
The world sparkling with bullets
With fire as dangerous as the sun
The world raining blood
The sun drowning in hatred and anger
Yet the war rages on
Darkness covered the world
And the light diminished as the war began
Yelling and screaming of the tiny children
The innocent children
Gone
Death pursuing lives of the fallen
Bombs as powerful as the earth
Gunfire as fast as light
And death coming before you could blink
Anger against the war
And yet we do nothing!

Mohammed Inqiyad Sadat (13)
The Bridge Academy, London

Your Eyes, A Deep Ocean

Your eyes, a deep ocean,
Penetrating into my soul.
It prevents any motion
The storm pushes me to you as if to bowl.

Your eyes, the sea
Is calm and serene . . .
It can't be free
Your eyes, the marine

Do you feel the same about me?
Do I rock your boat?
Would you like us to become a 'we';
United and free;
Or will you ship me off on a dreary moat?

Thunder, lightning can't keep us apart,
Through rain and storm I will appear!
God's art.
Everywhere you go,
Through thick and thin, I'm always near.

I can't stay away;
I need your heat, your breath on my ear.
It's as if I moulded your shape with clay,
The way your heart races without a care!
Oh, oh I need your body pressed onto mine
So fine, so very fine.

I need to sign off now my dear,
But I will forever treasure you my pearl,
My dear, never fear, just remember
Your eyes, a deep ocean . . .
Your eyes, the marine . . .

Bimpe Christianah Afolabi (12)
The Bridge Academy, London

 **Her Special Day**

The sun rays bounced off a mirror,
To reveal a bride of a brand new era,
Her glowing eyes filled with love,
As her and her partner become one.
Her contoured cheeks and shining teeth smiled with laughter,
No trace of disaster!
Her golden ring shone with a gleam,
Her cascading curls, tucked with pearls,
Her Louboutin shoes reminded her of you,
Her Balmain dress covered her chest.

Lilies and roses she held her bouquet,
She prayed to God, she'd have a good day.
Her father proud, her mother crying,
The church bells rang, as they started chiming.
Her bridesmaid laughed, soon they will dance,
'Catch the bouquet,' they hope with a chance.
Once you find love there's no going back,
'And trust me my dears, I am sure of that.'
Her ivory dress, fitted and flared,
Her sweetheart bodice sparkled and glared.

The cars have arrived, here she goes -
Just in time to steal the show.
She links arms with her father, she loves him so,
He says, 'That's my girl,' and off they go.
Hundreds of eyes stare at her clearly
But there's only one pair really appealing.
Her partner, her rock, her brand new husband,
Joined in matrimony, witnessed by dozens.
So here they are, no hurt, no lies -
As they start their new life, as husband and wife.

Jessica Tinubu (14)
The Bridge Academy, London

 # I'm The First Love

I'm the first love,
I'm a mascara stain,
On a young teen's face.
I'm the heartbreak,
Running through her veins.
I'm the betrayal,
That had caused her pain.
I'm the emptiness,
Inside the drops of rain.

She wants a god,
She wants a prophet.
She's praying for it to come out,
Yet she's stuck to be modest.
She begs to scream,
She pleads to shout.
But the words are trapped in her mouth.

The broken promises,
The heart-felt lies.
I promised myself,
You wouldn't defy.
I promised myself,
I wouldn't cry.

My mother calls me to come down,
I look at her shining crown.
My mum's my world, my mum's my shine,
Through my heartbreak she's been by my side.
She stuck with me when my grandad died.
She was right there when I had to say bye.

Zehra Sonerman (13)
The Bridge Academy, London

Outcast . . .

The anger builds up,
The calm gives up,
No one knows how it feels . . .
To be an outcast.

It struck me like a lightning,
Began to stop fighting,
I'm not Temperantia,
I'm not Benevolentia,
I'm an outcast.

But my hate filled me like a ball,
A thing kicked against the wall,
I cry every time,
But that's not a crime,
I'm not positive,
I'm not Humilitas,
I'm an outcast.

I like being modest,
But I'm not always honest,
I'm not Humilitas,
I'm not Castitas,
I'm an outcast.

Industria is just not me,
It sounds like I'd have to pay a fee,
All that is left
Is Dissimilis,
That's me,
I'm an outcast indeed.

Michael Wong (14)
The Bridge Academy, London

 # Society

I feel trapped,
Everywhere I go I feel trapped,
As if I'm on TV while everyone watching
Waits for my mistakes.

One step forward but they push me two steps back,
It's as if they lust for my mistakes like a vampire for blood,
In their eyes I can do nothing right.

I feel trapped,
Everywhere I go I feel trapped,
As if my head is being pushed underwater,
And I struggle to breathe.

They paint us all with the same brush,
Letting blotches of paint stain,
Seeping into the paper,
They want us to be the same colour,
To be the same.

They break the little girl with dreams,
The boy with hopes,
They let them burn and crumble,
What happened to being yourself?

In my head,
The lists of names,
Of what I've done wrong,
Carries on,
And this is what I slowly become.

I am trapped.

Nadia Rabbani (14)
The Bridge Academy, London

Love And Emotion

In this fearful moment,
I plead that you do not feel any pain,
That this could all go away,
Seeing you with a waterfall running down your face,
Makes my heart break
You are the sugar in my tea,
The butter on my bread,
The cherry on top of my cupcake,
We have to be complete,
What's tea without sugar
Butter without bread,
What's me without you
Although it pains me to say,
A tear is running down my face,
But I am a man I should be strong, courageous and brave,
But what man am I without you, I will find you one day my love,
Even though I wish you were here now I promise not to put on a frown,
No matter how far apart we are, we will be near in the mind and soul my dear,
My heart is aching for your love,
So I will hurry no matter what the weather,
In the raging storm, on the brightest day,
I know we will meet again one day,
Losing you will be my most nerve-wracking dream,
Even though a lie this may seem,
You are one of a kind,
Someone no one can replace,
I hope this poem has shown how strong my love is for you,
Always remember that I *will* find you . . .

Lynn Gezi (12)
The Bridge Academy, London

No Such Thing As Perfect

Deserted, trapped, alone
I can't stress it anymore
Stranded in a black cloud
My thoughts surround my disappearing soul
Angels around me, reassured me
Staying strong . . .
Truth teller; never lying
Yet they still do not understand
I don't understand,
Why?
Why do they not understand?
Restricted in confusion
Floating, glowing, empty
Yet focused
Nearer to consistency
My mind a regret of 'perfect'
Escaping through thoughts
Perfect?
Perfect is never perfect.
The blackness in the cloud fading
As my thoughts disappear
Left alone
Yet I realise we are all not the same
Confused: I'm a positive teenager
Living in a negative world,
an imperfect world,
a world where nobody's perfect.

Anneta Kamara (14)
The Bridge Academy, London

Memories

Things move too fast,
Everything I try to see goes by before I even notice . . .
The crowds of people rush by, each one of them loading off their luggage,
Packed with different items from a different life . . .
Then the train zooms off again,
Before I even get to say goodbye . . .

The car pulls up,
No expression on his face,
No life in hers . . .
We drive off, yet again . . .

I take one step into that house,
The pictures, the furniture; the memories come flooding back . . .
I run, fast.
Until I reach him . . .
I fall the floor, crying.
Crying my pain out,
The pain,
The pain is like there is a china ornament inside of me,
And every moment someone is smashing me, again and again and again . . .
And that person is her.
My pain is real.
So was his when he was lying on the ground, no one to save him.
'Dad!' I scream.
But he won't hear me . . .
He will never hear me, ever again.
He will be in eternal pain.

Pearl Phipps (12)
The Bridge Academy, London

Invisible

Do you know what it's like to be invisible?
I do
To cry tears of blood yet you're told you don't matter
To be unwanted, left to die, to rot
To think you're the reason for all the problems
To be one of the forgotten
Invisible
The past is the past (that's what they all say, don't they?)
But how can you forget what's pierced in your brain and burned in your heart?
What gives you nightmares and leaves you a zombie in the morning?
Invisible
But what if I drown in my own tears?
No one would notice
No one would care.
Invisible
But when I look in the mirror
I see shattered glass
It's not the reflection of me
But my heart
Invisible.

Lina Ali (13)
The Bridge Academy, London

Exam

The aroma leaks through my bones
Enclosing me in a confined room
Engulfed by darkness
I try to fight through it
But the paper stands straight
I get pushed back into an ongoing cycle of trauma
When I finish it I look back
And the cycle continues.

Saul Secka (13)
The Bridge Academy, London

Nation's Dispute

A never-ending rage,
The feud between two nations,
They will never be united as one nation.
Their bloodlust for each other,
Their emotions are neglected and rejected,
Which only makes their frustration projected.

Their fury is everlasting,
Their unfulfilled paths reflect their unsettled past.
Their strength undermines their temper,
Their physicality overpowers their mentality.

I tell you now,
The expression they put on,
Will not matter since
Their temptation will be gone.

Destruction is what they bring,
Competence is what they sing,
But bad vitality is what they think.

Never again.

Dion Fejzullahu (14)
The Bridge Academy, London

Demons

The storm rages on
As the justice inside of me
Struggles to hold in the demons
I am sorry if I sin
I am sorry if I rage
But the demons inside of me
Want to come out and play
My smile is only a facade
That hides my anger.

Ryan Neto Da Silva (13)
The Bridge Academy, London

Why Don't People Understand

Why don't people understand?
No one has the upper hand.

We are all outcasts black or white,
Every race has its own fight.

No one has perfect complexion,
No one has perfect religion.

And yet we still have to make a decision.

And the issues faced in the world today
Are the type of issues that lead you astray.

People judge me by the way I walk
People try to figure me out by the way I talk.

But . . .
Change who I am for the benefits of others?
How do I explain that to the God above us?

Why don't people understand?
Life is a massive game plan.

Aaliyah Hamzah (14)
The Bridge Academy, London

 # Mind Games

Scars of war lay in my mind,
The ground stained with blood,
My courage I cannot find,
The air poisoned
with death,
I glared at the godless wasteland,
barren and dead,
No sign of life,
not a breath.

Parteek Singh (13)
The Bridge Academy, London

Manufactured

We're told to act based on our stereotypical roles,
Being careful around each other,
Not to step on each other's toes
Everyone is different
Yet we're told to act the same
Trying to be a player
In this huge life game
Ladies wear your make-up
Do the chores
Whilst your man sits
And points out your flaws
This is how we are brought up
Manufactured so deep
Runs deep in the heart
So I ask you please
Be who you are
Otherwise we'll lose
Another shining star.

Aynur Yoruk (14)
The Bridge Academy, London

Blamed

I am so angry
I make lava look like a twig snapped in half
I am so angry
I made war and destruction with everybody bowing to me
I am so angry
I follow my first rule - keep my friends close but my enemies closer
I am so angry
I have the title 'I am the Prince of Darkness'
I am so angry
People don't dare to stand before me.

Albert Thomas James Andrews (11)
The Bridge Academy, London

One Day

One day I was born
And didn't know anything at all.
One day I saw people
Who were ever so tall.
One day I sat down and watched TV.
The other day I made friends at my nursery.
One day I moved schools
And the next day I learnt.
The other day I realised I did a lot of work.
One day I looked in the mirror
And saw myself grow and asked myself
What do I want to be when I'm older?
And then I saw for sure
I wanted to be an actress.
One day I was born
And knew after . . .
I wanted to be an actor!

Tricia Cecile (13)
The Bridge Academy, London

It's About A...

You would think he's a hard-boiled egg
Open it should be soft but it's all hard
Underneath is just like the outside

Seeing what I want to see, a nice person
I want to see the yolk in you but it's just not there
Loving you
Loathing you
You have a really hard shell to peel

Bothering myself to figure you out
Open up your shell
You're hurting my jaws, can't you see what you're doing to me?

Haleigh Gregory (12)
The Bridge Academy, London

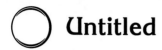
◯ Untitled

King of the marsh!
On the marsh, where birds sing
The kestrel is king
Where the kids all play
Voles can be prey
On the marsh where the kestrel is king

On the marsh there could be anything
The kestrel is king
As night turns to day
Voles can be prey
On the marsh where the kestrel is king

On the marsh there's a crow with an injured wing
And the kestrel is king
Voles have young in May
So watch out they could be prey
To the kestrel the king of the marsh.

Dylan McNally (11)
The Bridge Academy, London

Gullible Generation

Government's still dictated by those with power
Democratic views, forgotten in an hour
Opinions twisted by brain-washing media
Making us dumber and making us needier
Needier to hear the stereotypes
Influenced by the latest trends and hypes
Steered into the chaos like a moth to a flame
Swallowed by society, standards and fame
Drowned in a sea of new expectations
If they aren't met, expect accusations
It's 2015 and our world is corrupt
We're living in a volcano about to erupt.

Ray Bonsall (13)
The Bridge Academy, London

Racism Is The Bane Of My Existence . . .

There is an image in my mind,
It is very clear and easy to find.
To you I have a different personality,
You think I am addicted with insanity.

Racism is what I hate,
Just because I'm one of a kind,
You decide my own fate.
God is my creator, it's me who He made,
But you just retaliate and make my image fade.

I look myself in the mirror,
I ask myself why.
Tears stream down my face,
As I frantically cry.

Jawdat Nejim (13)
The Bridge Academy, London

Raisins

Raisins . . .
I hate raisins, I hate them with a passion
They taste like vomit mixed with dead rats
They look like bird droppings
That have merged together with old chewing gum
They smell horrible, so horrible
It makes you want to vomit for your whole life
Raisins are the worst food ever invented
They ruin everything from cake to cookies
And make them look like they're rotting
And make them taste like they're out of date
They are the bane of my existence
All raisins must be destroyed!

Riyad Hussain (12)
The Bridge Academy, London

Rage

My anger burns and rages at the close of day,
It shines down like the sun's ray,
Irritating with frustration,
It's like an open invitation.

My heart beats faster and faster,
In control of the master,
Rage, rage,
A feeling that happens in every age,

I would love to react,
Punch, kick, slap,
Anything to let the anger fade,
In my house,
The cleaning is done by a maid.

Abdirahim Mohammed Abdi (11)
The Bridge Academy, London

What Has Society Come To?

What has society come to?
Look at all of what they do
All we do is judge and hate
To those who fit the bait

All guns pointed at their faces
Shooting down the different races
But there ain't no actual cases
They divert our attention to other places

Help and love is all they need
They shoot at people like it's Assassin's Creed
Kill each other continuously like my Call of Duty feed
What has society come to?
But we may be able to pull through.

Afsana Yasmin (13)
The Bridge Academy, London

 # My Horse . . .

As green as a gem,
Green like the grass,
Its eyes sparkled like the sun,
Its mane raced down its neck,
Black as the night.
Its skin so deep, so dark,
The night it was like.

Its teeth were shiny
As the stars,
Its body silky and soft.

It's a horse of love . . .
My horse is my love,
To me.

Ahlam Moxamed (11)
The Bridge Academy, London

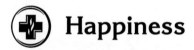 # Happiness

Nothing can compare, nothing at all
I love my friends, but my family more.
Birthdays, Christmas, New Year's Eve,
Celebrations where everyone can be happy.
I am a rainbow,
The world is a stage,
I look up to the sky as the sun shines on my face.
Everyone smiles, they're filled with joy,
This makes me happy, I love my life more.

Oh, how I love my mealtimes and it wouldn't be the same
If my friends and family were not here to make it okay
A brand new era, a brand new day
Always remember, happiness is the way.

Lydia Monka (13)
The Bridge Academy, London

Parents Forever

Mum, your skin is as smooth as silk,
Your eyes are glistening jewels,
You are precious to me as any gem,
Your hair is the colour of chocolate,
Your eyes are bright as a diamond.

Dad, you are my hero, like a brave lion in a fight,
When your team loses you are as angry as a bull at a red flag,
Your voice is soft like a monk.

Without both of you in my life,
I would be a sun without a moon
Or rain without sunshine.

I would be nothing.

Abubakar Omar (11)
The Bridge Academy, London

 # Thirteen

The day is coming,
The day is near.
When my life begins a new era,
When I am no longer a child.
A young man,
That's what they'll say.
Not a child anymore,
No time to play.
More responsibilities lie ahead.
So I can't just eat chocolate spread.
Have to care for others,
Can't be mean.
That's what will happen when I'm thirteen.

Teo Chinyelu-Hope (12)
The Bridge Academy, London

These Parts

The air is thick in these parts,
We aren't so quick in these parts.
The people slouch, stay in their house,
We're always skint in these parts.

Though children play in these parts,
Youths still spray in these parts.
They don't care, to leave walls bare
And fresh and clean in these parts.

I try to cope in these parts,
Try not to mope in these parts.
The culture's gone, it's all gone wrong,
Let's all get on in these parts.

Tyler Moran (14)
The Bridge Academy, London

Life Is Beautiful

As dark as my anger gets
My best friend is the best
Her love for the one I adore
Is bigger than it gets.
My footsteps quiet
My heart is silent
My mind is clear
I close my eyes and hear the fear
I grip my hands and hear the fear
I stretch my smile and see how far it goes
I move on with my day
And live life with hope
Every day I pray for peace
My thoughts for the one
I love will never end because
My heart, my heart cannot bend.

Rhea Pushkarna (12)
The Harrodian School, London

The Breakdown

We met as four,
Not knowing at all
That sooner or later
The code name was Wall.

The fights, the lies,
The midnight cries,
The constant fear
Throughout the year.

And suddenly, it all seems fine,
There's still a break between the line
But eventually it all comes back
The fights, the lies, it all turns black.

Then a new piece adds to the puzzle,
It seems to fit
And open heart
Forms a new fresh start.

But after those days
The pain comes back
And as before,
It all turned black.

We turned against Wall,
Not knowing at all
That the biggest mistake
Would cause our break.

We tried to fix all we could
But it was no use.
The pieces from our puzzle fell apart
And so did open heart.

And days passed later
With silence and sadness
While our situation
Grew with madness.

Now in the present
We all can see
That hope lies ahead
As the beginning first said.

But later they left me,
All bare and alone
It's the start of my breakdown,
Do they care? No they don't.

Sasha Falkovskaia (12)
The Harrodian School, London

◯ When I'm Older

When I'm older I want to be a fireman,
I can save people's lives all the time,
I can ride down poles at the speed of light.
I can climb up trees and save cats,
I can climb up ladders as high as the skies,
I think I might be a fireman.

Or when I'm older I could be a doctor,
I can ride around in ambulances all day,
I can listen to the thudding sounds of patients' hearts.
I can save people's lives with a wave of a hand,
I can bring new life to the world,
I think I might be a doctor.

I could consider that when I'm older I could be a gardener,
I can cut the bushes into nice shapes,
I can smell all the roses in the world,
I can talk to people admiring the daisies,
I can mow the grass into different patterns,
I think I might be a gardener.

I know whatever I am,
Whether it be a fireman,
A doctor or a gardener
I will love it all the same.

Izzie Whiting (12)
The Harrodian School, London

The Honour Killing

12pm
12 hours until death
The sun leaves an ominous glow
A shadow of pain
A shadow of sorrow
A shadow of the clock slowly ticking away my time.

1pm
I close my eyes
I need to let go of my past
As much as I try
As much as I resist
The memories just won't go away.

4pm
I've waited for hours
Time just doesn't seem to stop
I look out the window
I hold in my tears
As I say farewell to the sun.

7pm
5 hours until death
I still can shed no tears
I bang on the clock
It simply won't stop
Won't give a second
Won't give a minute to spare.

10pm
2 hours to go
I scream
I shout
And I pray
This is the end
This is my story
This is my very last day.

5 minutes to 12
They come for me
I see the silver blade
The clock strikes 12
I then go weak
And soon, I spring to my death.

Sonya Luchanskaya (12)
The Harrodian School, London

 # Have You Seen What's Happening Outside This Room?

Have you seen what's happening right
outside this room?
Bullets are being shot
and people are starting to fall.

Have you seen what's happening right
outside this room?
Forests are being burnt
and animals are suffering a lot.

Have you seen what's happening right
outside this room?
The skies are turning black
because the pollution is so bad.

Have you seen what's happening right
outside this room?

Gonzalo Castellanos (11)
The Harrodian School, London

Breakdown

I'm in the unit, sitting on my bed
Troubling thoughts smother my head
Nobody loves you, nobody cares
No one can hear the sound you can't bear.

Closing in all around me
Is a fear I can't describe
I'm shaky and confused
I think I'm going to die.

I have broken down
And my poor head aches
My heart pains
From previous mistakes.

I can't stop the tears
They fall like rain
And everything I feel
Is wracked with pain.

I was once so light
Now so slacked
When can I have
Those happy times back.

Darkness is closing in all around
But no one can hear a single sound
Closing in all around me
Is a fear I can't describe
All I want to do
Is break down and cry.

Zanthe Livingstone (12)
The Harrodian School, London

Dream Unstoppable

Tick-tock goes the clock,
My feet run down the tiny clock,
I'm in a nightmare,
Lost at thought sea,
Something terrifying is chasing me.

I'm all alone then I shiver,
I turn around to see a shady figure,
Wrinkled and old yet faster than me,
I have no choice I jump into the sea.

I can't swim, I can't breathe,
I can no longer see,
Down faster and faster I go,
My bones feel soft just like dough.

Then something grabs my throat,
This feels unreal till I start to choke,
I flip my arms back and forth,
I try to block my mind with fairy tales of dwarfs,
Release me of my pain that I wish was a dream,
Or just get this man off of me.

My skin starts to bleed as it scrapes the rocks,
And my eyes gouge out and stick to the docks,
Although I can't see I know a presence,
My childhood fear arrives like a present.

Then I wake up and feel relief
I turn around to see,
The shadowy figure wasn't a dream.

Luca Angelica Fuller (11)
The Harrodian School, London

He Ran Away

The aeroplane screeched to a halt.
The flight was all great
But never could I know my fate,
I had a yearn to see my shining star,
The one I loved above the rest.
Others couldn't, wouldn't understand.

We drove down the long gravel track,
The sky was grey, but I didn't mind,
I wanted to see my star.
My big heavy foot crunched upon the small gravel,
Each step I took got me closer,
Closer to my star.

I was sure, just too sure
But when I came in,
When I came in the door
I knew, I knew something was wrong.
Nobody had to say,
Because I knew my rabbit had run away.

Tabby Wellesley (11)
The Harrodian School, London

Brothers

Shouts and screams
Hits and smacks
This torture never ends
'I'm telling!'
'You're so stupid!'
I'm sick of him already
Whatever I do
Wherever I go
I'm always here
I'm Mummy's favourite.

Ruby-Rose Hutchings (12)
The Harrodian School, London

⚽ Football

Football, bouncing around all day
How fun it is to play
Rolling around, getting all muddy
Going in for tackles, getting all bloody.

Football putting the ball into the back of the net
At half-time eating a baguette
Working together with the team
When we win smoother than in cream.

Smashing the bar with a shot
Rebounding and hitting Grandma's pot
Smashing a window
Neighbours go bingo.

Football, bouncing around all day
How fun it is to play
Rolling around, getting all muddy
Going in for tackles, getting all bloody.

Adam Holt (12)
The Harrodian School, London

 # My Life

What is it like to be me,
Bearing all the things I do,
Rushing to lessons,
Confusing maths sums,
Complicated science equations,
Beady eyes on teachers,
Sending you out at will,
Crazy homework,
And parents, cruel and merciless,
Yet, it ends quite nicely
With a piping hot bath.

Ben Smith (12)
The Harrodian School, London

Joy

Joy is with you
He never left
Joy is happy
Right or left
Either way you go
He will know
Joy will glow.

Joy is with you
Hiding in a flower
Or in the ball you love to throw
He has the power
To change your way
When you start to fade.

Joy is with you
He never left
You just need to find it in your chest.

Coco Falconer (11)
The Harrodian School, London

 # WWII; One In A Million

Constant pounding, hammering through my skull,
His bullets are searching for me, looking, groping.
A click, and the heavy breathing of him punctuates the mist.
I can simply hide, too terrified to run,
I grip my gun with feeble hands.
Then silence.
A sudden string of screams whether they are mine I cannot tell,
My blood flees from my body,
Knowing I am doomed,
The four horsemen call, and I must answer.
I leave this world to see those I once loved,
To see those I once knew.

Maximillian Jameson (11)
The Harrodian School, London

What It Is Like To Be Me

I play games
but you call me names.
Whatever I do
you stop me doing it.

You say I'm crazy
but you don't know
about my life.
I wish you would go away.

I hate you
and you hate me.
I wish you would just stop
eating my life.

I'd like to think life is just a game
I wish you would just go away
because you are so lame.

Jack Owen (11)
The Harrodian School, London

Humilitas

Elena, Elena, Elena;
Your hair, your eyes
There's not one thing I don't love about you,
Your voice is sweet,
Your hair is neat
And these are things I like about you.

Your hair glistens through the darkness,
Your purple ends are nicest,
Your eyes are brown
But don't frown,
You're amazing,
Forever till the end.

Emma John (12)
The Harrodian School, London

Forces Of A Modern City

People hunched over, coughing,
The black, ashy gas moulds through a fence.
The diseased manner of smoke zips through vents.
Smoke is a descendent of fire.

The faint buzzing of a neon sign,
Its vibrant colours blink.
Its illuminous features
Light up the night.

The pixilated whir of a disc.
The imagination video can create.
The industrial black case of a square, blue, free world.

The rough hard soul
Of concrete shrapnel.
Cold, mean and sharp
Piercing any heart.

Alexander Mulcahy (12)
The Harrodian School, London

 # Power

Kings and queens, with no power
Politicians' strict control
Striving, trying to get a job
Heartless, remorseless, sheds no love.

Diseases spreading by the hour
Pollution growing, leaving only a flower
Wars rage on, weapons are developed
Biological war, is the new steam engine.

Villages, cities, civilisations
All of which are human creations.

Alejandro Pond (12)
The Harrodian School, London

The Problem With Father Christmas

Father Christmas climbed down the chimney,
He got stuck and cried,
And thought no one could hear me,
Oh but the milk and cookies are out of reach,
Then Rudolph saw a bird and started to screech.

The children woke up with a fright,
And whacked him hard with all their might.
'It's me, it's Santa!' they heard him cry,
'If you let me out, I'll give you a Fanta.'

They pulled and pulled
And Santa finally got loose,
But instead of a Fanta
They got a chocolate mousse.

Heidi Solman (11)
The Harrodian School, London

The Street

My footsteps echo down the long, dark street
As I step, raindrops fall all around
The street lights flicker from on to off
Lightning strikes the nearby houses.

A distant sound of a dog crying help
Laughing, from a cheerful house
The moon is out, shining bright through the cloud
The stars are not, shrouded from sight.

A cat screeches from an alley, near to me
The houses turn grey as I slowly stroll on
Leaves blow past my shivering legs
The trees sway on, in the cold night's wind.

Jasper Mortimer (11)
The Harrodian School, London

I Love

I love the trees

How they dance in the wind
How they smell like a fresh summer's breeze
How they smile when the sun touches their face

I love the moon

How it smiles down at us
How its love spreads throughout the town
How its white face stands out in the pitch-black background

I love roses

How their red cheeks stand out in others
How their rosy petals smell like a fresh summer's day
How their stems stand tall in the soft grass

I love.

Emilia Pinto (12)
The Harrodian School, London

 **Photography**

Photography is great
You capture good times with your mate
Black, white or colour
You can take a picture with your brother.

Change the setting to sport
It shows how people fought
Contestants want to win
They will do anything like jump in a bin.

The camera can zoom in
To capture something like a pin
It's a career you can make
But something you can't fake.

Mia Lapwood (11)
The Harrodian School, London

The Bookshop

This mall needs another stairway I'm told;
Shops, clothes, sweets and toys head towards nowhere.
Do they want us to come from the same mould?
I'd rather have books than new clothes to wear.
Debenhams, Burger King, moving stairway -
Monuments to lack of effort and thought.
Big companies look at us like we're prey
Dressing us up, leaving our minds to rot.
Westfield needs a Foyles, a boundless bookshop;
Westfield doesn't need a moving stairway.
It may raise us, but we won't be the top.
Will knowledge disappear or break away?
Will fashion beat books in the fight for glory?

Will great books be torn from the world's story?

Memphis Grace MacPherson (12)
The Harrodian School, London

 # Fading Away

Fading away in the dark
Nothing passes by
Soldiers die
We cry
Fade away, fade away, fade away
Now they have gone
And it was so long
Fade away, fade away, fade away
We are sad
And they are mad
We should stop it now
They eat our souls
And take control
Fade away, fade away, fade away.

Santa-Elise Cohu Davies (11)
The Harrodian School, London

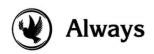

Always

Life, simple for most, dull for none.
The day shall come when I am none.
Could be today, could be tomorrow.
The day shall come leaving many in sorrow.
I have loved. I have giggled. I have smiled
And I have wept.
The day shall come when I am lying in that hospital bed.
Stop, don't pity me!
I don't want your sympathy!
The day shall come when I am dead.
When my bones are aching and my feet can't climb the stairs.
Stop, don't pity me!
I don't want your sympathy!
Love Grandma.

Sophia Baranowski (12)
The Harrodian School, London

The Black Wedding Dress

It's twelve o'clock
He's still not back
The sorrow in my heart
Collides with black

My desk is full
Of drenched tissues
My mind is crossing my pain
Got to fix these issues

It's one o'clock
He's still not back
I hide myself
In a tight crack.

Ginevra Benedetti (12)
The Harrodian School, London

Friendship

Friends, what a wonderful thing
Sometimes they make you want to sing.
Friends are great to care
They won't make you feel despair.

Friends won't let you down
Otherwise it will make you frown.
Sometimes friends will make you cry
And your friendship won't be able to fly.

But at the end of the day
With your anger put away
You can turn all the bends
And you will always be friends.

Takumi Nakamigawa (12)
The Harrodian School, London

Untitled

Dark sky, inside my heart,
Rainy day, I feel upset,
Sometimes, I think I'm lost
Deep, deep inside my heart.

All I need are friends to talk to,
I don't need those who often lie,
Most people cheer me up,
When I'm feeling quite sad.

Friends often make me smile,
I smile all the time,
When someone says horrible things
I always try not to cry.

Aisha Hotei (12)
The Harrodian School, London

Friendship

Your friend sits by your side,
They do not run and hide,
If you are in a muddle,
They will give you a cuddle.

If you are sad,
They do not make you mad,
If you don't understand
And you are stuck in the sand
They will help you with the whole lot,
Even if you don't know a lot.

Your friend sits by your side,
They do not run and hide.

Francesca Drayson (11)
The Harrodian School, London

The Easter Bunny

On a morning that was fairly sunny,
Out hopped a special bunny,
He hid the eggs one by one,
And dived into a bush when he heard the children come.

Their squeals of delight made him smile,
The little eggs soon turned into a pile,
'So much chocolate!' cried out the little girl,
'If I eat it all, I think I might hurl!'

The special bunny soon made a retreat,
He gave another house the same lonely treat.
If you see him, you are very lucky,
For this little creature is the Easter bunny.

Yasmine Salloum (11)
The Harrodian School, London

Child Life

An innocent child with a face never red
Is living a free, relaxing life, like being in bed
But in that child is a very strong heart
Which is scared of childhood coming apart.

Scared of talking to imaginary friends
Worried that she can't feed the hens
Amazed that every day might be bad
Or living in misery feeling sad.

But having the thought is getting enough
And she's not worried about growing up.

Florence Durond-Deslongrais (12)
The Harrodian School, London

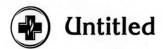

Untitled

Poems, they are the most amazing thing.
New knowledge to our world they bring.

Usually, at the end of each line is the occasional well-placed rhyme.
To write them can take quite a long time
But if you have patience then you should be fine.

Their words can make us face our fears
Or otherwise bring us close to tears.

As you all know, poems are an extraordinary thing,
They are what let our emotions sing.

Wieger Dop (11)
The Harrodian School, London

Love

Love is a word, often heard,
Is it a passion or does it flutter like a bird?
Discriminate isn't the word to mend you together,
Love is meant to be forever and ever.

Love is a word, often heard,
The way it makes you feel is quite absurd.
Just inhale the power, no need to be shy
Love is incredible it can make you cry.

Sophia Klat (12)
The Harrodian School, London

 # Imagine

Imagine your daughter coming home from school
She tells you she has no friends.
Imagine your two-year-old son looking you in the eyes,
Asking you if you care.

And, when your wife asks you what's wrong,
You reply, 'It's nothing.'
She thinks you mean you're fine,
When really, you're empty, it haunts you forever.

Cengiz Uran (12)
The Harrodian School, London

 # Untitled

Oh chocolate cake, beautiful chocolate cake,
How you leave a flavoursome taste in my mouth,
Making every move after feel amazing
The brown fluffy cakes make my lips hum
And drop to the ground.
You're a gift for me and my mouth,
Please never leave my side!
Rest in peace after I have eaten you.

Lara Jiryes (11)
The Harrodian School, London

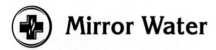 # Mirror Water

Water calms my soul.
Oh sweet water, you cleanse my dirty flesh,
Oh chanting water, you summon my thoughts of peace,
Extinguishing my anger.
Oh clear water, mirroring my nature, sorting out my life.
Oh dear water, my love for you is endless,
I need you, oh water. . .

Geronimo Hayaux du Tilly (13)
The Harrodian School, London

Fury

Red as blood.
Scarlet as Snow-White's apple.
A red cloud hanging over you.
As it grows, it rains on other people too.
When it grows lengthways, it grows upwards too.
The only umbrella is family.
Fury.

Archibald Pritchett (11)
The Harrodian School, London

Pandas

Pandas are cuddly
Pandas are sweet
But they are definitely not OK to eat
They nibble your fingers
They nibble your toes
But that's OK I suppose!

Megan Kelly (11)
The Harrodian School, London

Ode To Sun

The golden light shimmering onto the lakes
While your bony white skin becomes golden and opaque
The ice cream drips onto the wafer cone
While simultaneously you play on your favourite phone
The luscious pink roses lying right by
Are complimented by the relaxing sound of a hose outside.

Elena Chetayat (11)
The Harrodian School, London

◯ I Question

I question, what has come of this world today.
Sorrowful tears are shed as the hearts of many decay.
Skyscrapers go beyond the skies.
Symbols for what will emerge . . . the eye.
The devious eye, that weeps cackling tears. The eye that screams.
We will all be blind but still be able to see.
Many led by one-eyed cheats. White lies.
The rubble of fallen monuments has crushed many.
All around the world poverty is amidst. Whether you're homeless or whether
many children stay tearful and hungry.
The real question is, what has come of humanity?

Mankind is infested in greed, thus forgetting about others' needs.
Those others who drown in their own sorrows as I speak.
I question, should this not be regarded as insanity.
But as usual, a blind eye is turned by humanity.
Men and women scream, a new lease of life is what they try to but cannot
reap.
They are not yet free.
What is the ulterior intention? Is it to pinpoint misconceptions or are you
merely intending to deceive us with inception - and mental mesmerisation?
You lack accuracy and the correct mentality.
I question whether you have found the answer.
Although, I question . . . can this be classified as a canined conundrum?
Not in my eyes.

I question . . . do you not know?
I would like to ask whether there is hope.
Is the answer . . . no?
Share the prosperity.
Ensure some clarity, via charity.
Look around, all you see is poverty.
Oh . . . wait, I forgot you were blind . . . then you ask, why is this happening to
me?
Ice-like cries symbolise the demise, the demise that sends devilish shivers
down my spine.
That is something I can see.
But you are blind and hide from this truth so I have had to read it out to you.

Fawaz Khan (13)
Woolwich Polytechnic School For Boys, London

Life As A Teenager

What to say, what to do. Stand with you, or stand with you?
As soon as I walk in the door, all eyes on me so I try to avoid any eye contact
cos it opens a door for conversation, like I want that.
Not looking for extra attention, I just want to be just like you,
You know what they say, the nail that sticks out gets hammered . . . I think
that's all too true.
But I don't want to be a sheep, I want to be a shepherd.
A leader. I used to think that it was the way to go, but now I think it's time to
go.

I used to think that people followed others just to get recognition.
Take a minute to think about who this poem is dissing.
I used to think that all that safety in numbers was just a bunch of meaningless
words.
Now what do I see? Animals running in herds. Factions forming.
People fighting just to get recognition, then they think they're the business.
School. A prime example.
A place of education where people my age should be setting an example.
People are caught in the act. Detention? Hah, that don't mean jack!
They say that people change. Not in my eyes.
Once a hooligan, always a hooligan.

Amidst the war of cultures, there I am.
Watching every bruise, cut and gash being delivered. Every punch, kick and
headbutt.
I don't sit there wishing I was in the middle of it and putting the hurt on my
enemies
I sit there thinking, *what a pity.* Time wasted, blood tasted.
Wondering what others think of me has never been a worry,
How I'd like to be able to sit here with a straight face and say that.
The truth is I never stop thinking. Thinking but not caring.

When I first started secondary school,
I can honestly say that my insecurities could've eaten me alive.
I was always worried about what people would say.
But now I don't care all that much. I care of course, but just not as much as
you'd expect.
If someone has something to say, say it to my face.
Don't melt and spread a rumour. Have the balls to say it in front of me.
Cos if I've got something to say, I'll say it in front of you all and I'm not going to
be forced to sugar coat it all.

So this is my story so far.
This is to all you natural born leaders out there, don't succumb to peer pressure, just be true to you.
Because at the end of the day, they'll never amount to anything as great as you will.
You know why? Because they're just useless pawns being played by a greater player, looking to play you.

Mark Robertson (14)
Woolwich Polytechnic School For Boys, London

 # This World

The balance of life has destroyed the world
As every night we lie in the shadows embracing the cold
In the place where the moon meets the broken shadows
Causing tears to roll across the scars, no mere vessel can see
As the days continue to pass foreshadowing the prophecy we have been told

All the past generations have been manifested with discrimination
For this is the cause of our future annihilation
As the age of fear trembles in desolation
For this was the genesis of the proclamation

For so long we have been blinded from the truth
And told to speak knowledge to those in their youth
The very existence of this world is enveloped in flames, fire and decay
As it is awakened by the silent screams crying for peace.

Life had become a distant memory
An illusion in the past
As the memories we held so dear to our hearts have been sent avast
Our dreams and ambitions have been buried in the soil we were once formed
As our world . . . has become a speck in the face of darkness
A result of an apocalyptic infestation . . .

Jeremiah Kimuli (14)
Woolwich Polytechnic School For Boys, London

The Forgotten Ones . . .

There is a Syrian boy in a war-torn ravaged home,
Where his people eradicate each other just for the throne.
Blood is way cheaper than water for them to spill
With pernicious guns and grenades each other they kill.

He says, 'My peers in other worlds are centuries ahead of me
And I am here uneducated, striving to set me free.'

His dear mother was hit by a huge blazing shell.
Their daily life was from the tomatoes she used to sell.

His sister got dismissed from school because of the fee.
She was intelligent but who spared a moment to see?

His father was a drug-addict and robber in the street.
When something went wrong he would torture them and beat.

On a faithful morning they were notified of his death,
After parade of bullets riddled him below the head.

It was so tragic to him and so much worse than a thunder.
For, he'd at least sponsored him when no one did bother.

As a poor unlearned Syrian boy, he still polishes the shoes.
He could have been a millionaire, a politician on the news.

His clan is better, is what tore his great country apart
And let predators towards them make a cunning dart.

They paid allegiance to tribalism which caused disarray
Shrouded women and children in layers of dismay.
Some of those that fled get discriminated against every day.
Mercilessly stoned to death, on streets, while they lay.

I pray for the great country to rise up again,
So open your eyes world if you want to see Syria again.

Abdullahi Yusuf Abdullahi (14)
Woolwich Polytechnic School For Boys, London

The Wars That No One Wanted

There once was a war, a war that no one wanted
Fuelled by blood and rage and one man's desire.
There once was a war, a war that no one wanted
Where millions of fathers and sons deceased.
There once was a war, a war that no one wanted
Where the night sky was not lit by warm, inviting lanterns but furious, deadly explosions.

There once was a war, a war that no one wanted
Where peace never came.
There once was a war, a war that no one wanted
Which some called the Great War but war will never be great.
There once was a war, a war that no one wanted
That brought tension, sorrow and the rich to borrow.

There once was a war, a war that no one wanted
That still rages on in people's minds today.
There once was a war, a war that no one wanted
Where men burrowed like mice and decayed.
There once was a war, a war that no one wanted
That took thousands of lives each day.

So let's stop the wars, the wars that no one wants
And make sure there are no crying widows or young orphans today.
Let there be peace in the world.
Let the hate be demolished utterly. Let the wars cease.
There shall never be a war, a war that no one wanted.

Hassan Farooq
Woolwich Polytechnic School For Boys, London

Still I Rise

My pale brown eyes and my bright light skin
Cause misjudgement about my soul from within
Normally perceived as an unclean negative soul
Tells me how little you know
This constant misjudgement causes constant detentions
Makes my mind feel angry and neglected
I don't fight back because that would cause more self-issues
Instead I deal with pain and stress-causing anxiety
You can grin saying petty little lies
Saying I'm the rudest boy telling other teachers lies
I get in so much trouble, to my parents it's no surprise
But at the end of the day like air I rise
But at the end of the day like dust I rise
But at the end of the day like foam I rise
Forced to stand in the middle of the classroom being glared at by mocking eyes
Still I rise because God is the unseen observer and a faithful judge
And he will adjudicate.

Gerald Adu-Sarkodie
Woolwich Polytechnic School For Boys, London

Refugee Camp

Happy, shining, glistening, free,
Why is it this can't be me?
I pull my curtain to find a cotton blanket,
Laid upon the surface of our sacred soil,
Tree branches transformed into white,
Glimmering and shimmering in the winter sunlight.

But not everyone worships this overspread drape
And not everybody loves its enjoyable chill,
Without warmth or a fire at their side,
People are left to freeze in the pale glow.
They scan in search of food and water,
Only to find a recipe for disaster.
Neither food nor water, what does it mean?
Frozen bodies left in the sinister, sparkling snow.

James Frederick Mark Simmons (14)
Woolwich Polytechnic School For Boys, London

YOUNG WRITERS
INFORMATION

We hope you have enjoyed reading this book – and
that you will continue to in the coming years.

If you're a young writer who enjoys reading and creative
writing, or the parent of an enthusiastic poet or story writer,
do visit our website **www.youngwriters.co.uk**. Here you
will find free competitions, workshops and games, as well
as recommended reads, a poetry glossary and our blog.

If you would like to order further copies of
this book, or any of our other titles, give us a
call or visit **www.youngwriters.co.uk.**

Young Writers,
Remus House
Coltsfoot Drive,
Peterborough,
PE2 9BF

(01733) 890066 / 898110
info@youngwriters.co.uk